A SHIP SO FAR

A SHIP SO FAR

A Seaman's Tales

Paul James

The Book Guild Ltd
Sussex, England

The Book Guild Ltd,
25 High Street,
Lewes, Sussex

First published 2000
© Paul James 2000

Set in Times
Typesetting by IML Typographers, Chester, Cheshire
Printed in Great Britain by
Bookcraft (Bath) Ltd, Avon

A catalogue record for this book is
available from the British Library

ISBN 1 85776 422 6

INTRODUCTION

A sea so deep,
A harbour that's near,
A good night's sleep, maybe ...

The shipping clerk's finger was definitely pointing in my direction. My pulse quickened; could it be my turn at last? I shot to the reception desk window.

'James, you'll be joining the *Libra* as Sixth Engineer.'

After weeks of standing by as a relief engineer on just too many vessels, at last I was joining one to sail on to foreign parts – Christmas 1959 was certainly going to be a whole lot different to any of those before.

It also looked as if one little mystery that had puzzled me since joining the company months previously was going to remain just that, at least for the foreseeable future. Why did the company seem determined to keep their office staff and administrators well apart from the seagoing staff, with the Superintendent's offices being located well apart from their main offices? Could it be that the seafarers were not considered suitable beings to fraternise with the shore staff?

'Chief, can I offer you a lift?'

It seemed a good idea to try and get off on the right footing with the Chief Engineer, particularly as I happened to know he didn't have any transport of his own. The expression on the Chief's face spoke volumes, there was no doubt at all what was passing through his mind – a still wet behind the ears junior engineer with four wheels and me, ten years a chief and still on shank's pony.

What limousine the Chief thought he'd be travelling in I

couldn't imagine but as we turned the corner into the car park, his forward momentum abruptly ceased, his jaw dropped as he stared ahead. Obviously reassurance was urgently required.

'It may have been built in 1936, Chief, but it hasn't let me down yet,' I said, feeling just a little guilty.

Actually, just a few weeks previously it had managed to bring a not insignificant car rally to a grinding halt as it stalled on a completely flooded road at a most unfortunate location, preventing the following cars from proceeding on their way.

Then there was the case of my disappearing sister, whose seat dropped rather dramatically towards the road after a floorboard collapsed when the car returned to the road following a somewhat impromptu flight over a humpback bridge. Now was certainly not the time to enlighten the Chief about these little dramas.

The Chief shrugged his shoulders, presumably far from convinced that he was doing the right thing but apparently resigned to his fate if he was going to save travelling expense. We set off, with me listening intently to his directions, my palms becoming uncomfortably sweaty as I concentrated on my driving; nevertheless, we arrived safely in no time at all.

Having accomplished the first hurdle with relative ease, I should have been feeling quite confident but as I changed into my working gear, doubts and anxieties flooded my thoughts. Would I adapt to the seagoing life and its demands? So much to learn and very little time to do so but there was no backing out now – it was a case of pressing on regardless.

Just two years previously when I desperately felt the need to change direction, I pursued a childhood ambition and tried to join the flying duties branch of the RAF – I pressed on regardless at that time but they couldn't decide whether they wanted me or not. They invited me back to RAF Hornchurch for a second bite of the cherry but as I couldn't establish why they hadn't been too impressed with me on the first occasion, there didn't seem much point in going through their extremely demanding testing procedures again – after all, I hadn't chosen to experience the unbelievable frustration of my seat somehow managing to come adrift in the flight simulator, with the rudder bar and stick disappearing out of reach.

On reflection, possibly my chances of survival at sea would be a little better, particularly if the RAF secured the seats in their combat aircraft in the same way as their flight simulators.

'Fire – Sixer, yes that's you laddie. In your car and telephone for the fire brigade – the box is half a mile down the road – then come straight back.'

The Chief was not joking – I ran as fast as I could to my car.

His orders had galvanised me into action but I couldn't do likewise with my car. Not a sign of life from the engine as the starter motor churned over.

'I just don't believe it, sod you,' I kept repeating. I ran down the road, found the phone – the handset was missing. Oh, my God what next. 'Where's the nearest phone?' I croaked at a passing cyclist.

'Dock entrance I think, mate,' he replied.

Feeling totally defeated, with my legs weakening and the prospects of no ship to sail on, I staggered into the next phone booth and on hearing a reply from the emergency service, gasped, 'The *Libra* is on fire, I'm the Sixth Engineer.'

'Thank you for your call but we are already aware,' was the response. No sooner had I replaced the handset than a posse of fire engines swept through the dock entrance and straight past me. Must get back to the ship – only hope the Chief doesn't find out about my misadventures, I thought.

Arriving breathless on board, I could clearly see smoke issuing forth from the engine room entrance. A fire officer was doing battle with his waterproofs. I knew exactly how he must be feeling – not sure whether to proceed without them and get soaking wet or try and persuade the sodding gear to slide up his legs as they have done a thousand times before with no trouble.

I decided it was high time I showed my face down below.

'Sixer, where the hell have you been? A fuel tank has ignited – a bloody rivetter working without a fire watcher inside the tank.' The Chief was fuming also, probably more than the fuel tank. 'Make sure everyone's out of the engine room and the boiler room apart from the firemen and ourselves,' he added.

Fortunately the first warning had achieved a dramatic evacuation of the vessel so at least it looked as if I might succeed in carrying out the Chief's orders with some degree of credibility at last.

'You won't forget today in a hurry, Sixer,' the Chief remarked after the fire was extinguished.

The fire brigade had done a good job, with little damage sustained despite all the smoke, drama and anxiety.

That experience was sufficient to convince me of the need for proper fire drills and training – something I'm still concerned with to this day but in a different role.

I could only think that it must have been the fire that had diverted my attention from what I was now trying to work out as I looked down the engineers' accommodation alleyway.

For the first time, I noticed what appeared to be a distinct pattern of footprints which started on the alleyway deck and, veered up the bulkhead before returning very neatly to the deck, with this pattern repeating itself. It struck me that some people's idea of a joke was beyond the pale – little did I know how those actual footsteps had come about.

'You'll be on watch with the Third Engineer. Do exactly what he says and if you're in doubt, ask him to explain.' The Chief's orders seemed clear enough, I just hoped the Third would tolerate my lack of experience and knowledge of seagoing matters.

Steam machinery had me hooked from being a lad but this was going to be entirely different. Would the reality of an hour-by-hour close encounter helping to operate and maintain this machinery prove to be what I had imagined? More importantly, would I be able to measure up to the required standards?

Well, the day of reckoning was rapidly drawing close and I'd soon be finding out – one way or another.

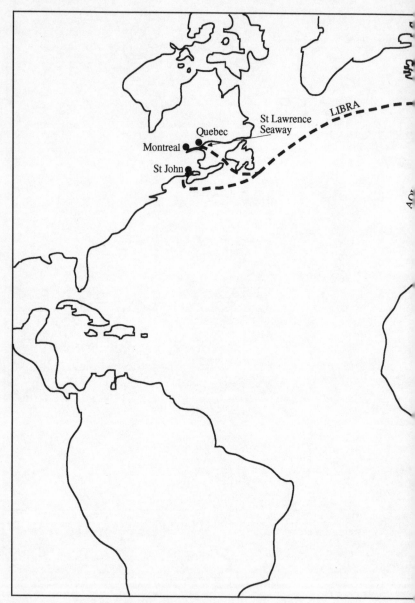

VOYAGE ROUTES 23.12.59 UP TO 23.12.63

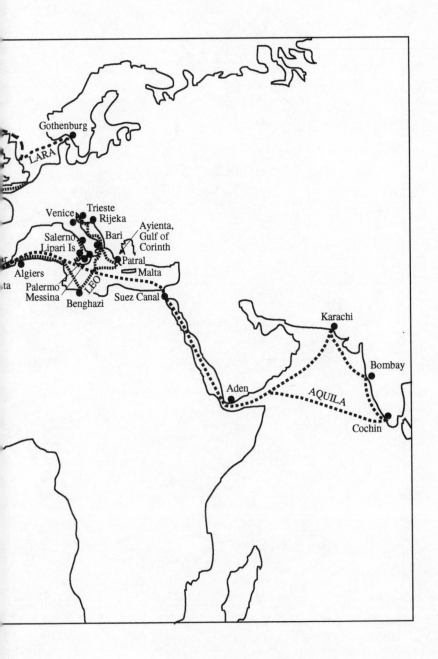

1

'During the summer this vessel trades up the St Lawrence seaway in Canada but during the winter when the seaway is frozen, we navigate the great circle northern route to Saint John in New Brunswick.' The Second Mate was an exceedingly cheerful type of person who couldn't also help adding that I would soon find out whether or not I had sea legs. I felt reasonably confident because I had experienced some uncomfortable weather during holiday trips round the coast of Britain without succumbing to the usual effects, but little was I to know what awaited me in the not too distant future.

'This weather is unbelievable,' was about the only comment I could think of as I tried to keep over end with the vessel performing combined pitching and rolling movements in a corkscrew fashion. I was told that the wind and sea conditions were northwesterly force 9 to 10; I certainly had no intention of going on deck to find out more. Although I didn't feel exactly on top of the world, nevertheless seasickness hadn't overtaken me and it looked as if my only suffering, apart from tiredness, would be a mother and father of headaches.

Watchkeeping was proving to be extremely demanding but everything was beginning to fall quite nicely into place and as the days passed the Third Engineer was spending less time down below. I misguidedly thought that this was due to his increasing confidence in my capabilities but it turned out to be more dictated by his own reaction to the bad weather. Of course he didn't advise this to me, so, quite naturally, I began to feel increasingly capable but forever reminding myself of the continual need to keep checking that everything was running smoothly, in particular trying to

1

make sure the four boilers had the correct levels of water – not all that easy when the water chases up and down the sight glasses like demented spirits.

As we approached Newfoundland, the heavy movements of the vessel eased but then blizzard conditions took over – the first of many white-outs I would come across. I don't know what it was about my first arrival at Saint John that struck me the most; it certainly was excruciatingly cold, never in my life had I imagined how uncomfortable such cold could be. The only apparel that seemed capable of coping with such cold was our doeskin uniforms, not the usual dress for venturing ashore in but, with the addition of pullovers and heavy overcoats, we felt that at least the cold could be kept at bay for a while. But even with that bodily protection, the cold penetrated one's face, nostrils and lungs, leaving one aching and gasping with pain as if icicles were attacking from within.

Even if one accepted the cold then certainly the remoteness and isolation of the place, right up the Bay of Fundy, made me sure that wild horses wouldn't drag me to live there if it meant that one could not escape until the winter receded. Probably I was over-reacting to the hostile winter environment; after all, for the several thousand residents there were plenty of bars, a few cinemas and the odd dance hall or two and, what's more, they seemed to accept their lot with considerable fortitude.

I just prayed that the deck machinery would not let us down; trying to carry out repairs in such conditions was a gruesome thought. It was a marvel that the stevedores persevered with the discharge of our cargo. They certainly earned their pay packets.

'Next trip, Sixer, it should be less cold and you'll be able to venture ashore at night, provided I don't need you on board.' The Second Engineer had obviously detected my disappointment at not getting ashore on my first trip.

Even the return voyage to the UK was uneventful, with the weather being reasonably favourable, and I couldn't wait to be relieved on arrival so I could get ashore and bore my friends and family with the story of my second great adventure.

My first had taken me right round Europe by motorbike when I was 19, with two friends. Apart from a catastrophic single error of navigation on my part in Germany, it was a resounding success. One lesson I learnt from that error was never to rely on one's memory for place names, particularly foreign ones – the shock of seeing the Swiss frontier post coming into vision when I thought we were close to Frankfurt after driving 150 miles in the wrong direction, was a never to be forgotten experience, as was the reaction of my friends.

Only two factors helped me survive at that moment in time – I had already navigated over 2,500 miles without error and the names of the two towns that had fooled my memory: Freiburg near the Swiss border and Friedberg near Frankfurt in Germany. The traffic diversion due to roadworks near Karlsruhe had an awful lot to answer for.

'Come on, Paul, what was it really like?' my friends from ashore demanded to know.

'To be honest, I don't really know where to start,' I said. I told them about the footsteps that I'd seen going up the bulkhead on the *Libra* when I'd first joined the vessel and I left them in no doubt that they hadn't come about as a result of a joke. Certainly when a ship is rolling heavily, the bulkheads become part of the walking areas if only for a few seconds. But I supposed what I'd noticed the most was the requirement to use all of one's senses when on duty in the engine room. After all, the Chief had told me before we sailed, 'Sixer, to do the job in a proper manner, you'll need to remember that your hearing, sense of smell, touch and taste count just as much as what you see.' To be honest I've always felt the Chief's advice regarding the last sense was more to do with off-watch activities and the contents of drinking glasses than duties in the engine room.

2

'Is the weather always as bad as this?' I enquired of the Second Mate.

Once again the vessel was performing in an unbelievable manner as we headed back across the Northern Atlantic, or the Western Ocean, as most seafarers call it, towards Saint John.

'I'm afraid so, Paul. That's why we don't carry passengers during the winter period.'

Once again the Third Engineer chose to delegate all the watch-keeping duties to me. He explained that he had a lot of paperwork to deal with but I guessed I knew better.

We arrived at the entrance to the Bay of Fundy in daylight hours whilst I was off watch so, despite the biting cold, I ventured on deck to capture what I could of the quite splendid scenery unfolding before me although I was extremely doubtful whether my camera was capable of operating in such a low temperature.

It appeared that we would be staying at Saint John for quite a while this time, for some unexplained reason, therefore when the Second Engineer stuck to his promise and granted me a half-day off, I decided to venture ashore while the going was good.

Much to my astonishment and despite the cold and the depth of snow, the buses were running, single-deckers admittedly, but in conditions that would have grounded their British counterparts. To board a bus and be asked by the driver for your fare was, once again, a first for me, resulting in an extremely embarrassing delay whilst I endeavoured to penetrate the depths of my outer garments to reach my money. My embarrassment was not eased by the suggestion of one hirsute passenger dressed in the obligatory checked shirt, trapper's hat and rifle to hand, that it might help if I put a bit

4

of hair round the target area! The response from the other passengers was at least predictable – mainly loud guffaws from the males, tut-tuts and much head-shaking from the ladies. I wished to hell that I'd never boarded the wretched bus but, at last, I produced what was causing all the fuss – my purse.

'He's found it,' my trapper friend quietly announced to all as my purse appeared from what must have seemed, to those staring in my direction, the region of my trouser fly. 'It's the cold weather, you know. Makes it disappear.' He was in full flow now. I tried to think of a suitable response as I passed down the aisle; I changed my mind as the source of my embarrassment came into view – he needed both seats to accommodate his frame. The wretched bus was nearly full and it wasn't until I had almost reached the back that a vacant seat appeared, and that was next to what I was almost sure was a very pretty lass but it was extremely difficult to tell as she was almost buried in her clothing.

'May I?' I enquired of her expectantly.

'What?' she replied in a puzzled manner.

'Sit next to you,' I almost pleaded.

'Sure, there's no law against that.'

'Thanks. That was very embarrassing, believe me,' I added for good measure.

Being sat at the back, she obviously hadn't been a party to my abject performance.

'Oh, you mean Butch,' she said. 'Has he been having a whack at you? Can't help himself. Just ignore him, like everyone else – the girls round town think he's a mental case.'

'I can tell you, that makes me feel a whole lot better. By the way, my name's Paul, I'm from the *Libra*. You know, it's the first time I've been on one of your buses, never had to pay the driver before, took me completely by surprise.'

We chatted on. Her name was Anne-Marie.

'I'm pretty sure you're where you say you're from because there's only one ship here at the present time. Say, Paul, do you dance?'

'A little, why?'

'Well, there's a hop at the Seamen's Mission tonight, so you can ask me along if you like.'

5

'That would be just great,' I replied. 'Except for one slight problem: it's my turn as duty engineer tonight.'

'Well then,' she said, 'I'll come down to the ship to see you.'

'That could also be a problem. The Captain won't allow any females on board unless they are accompanied by him.'

'Shucks, Paul, your life's full of complications. Can't be much fun.'

I almost felt like agreeing with her. Should I take a gamble and try and fix something up to meet her later? But knowing my luck, the whole thing would more than likely backfire and then, no doubt, she would remind me of my shortcomings.

'Guess you're right, Anne-Marie. Life's not exactly a ball game at present.' I decided it was time to quit. Maybe Butch was more her type, full of bull droppings and bonhomie, so to speak.

'Hey, come on, Paul, no need to play the little hurt boy with me,' she said, as I stood up to get off the bus. She grabbed me by the coat-tails and as all heads turned in our direction, I crashed back onto my seat with a sickening crunch and more acute embarrassment.

'We're only halfway to town, you silly so-and-so. You'd freeze to death if you tried to walk it; look, I'm sorry, Paul, but can't you just fix something up with one of your buddies – you know, swap shifts or whatever you call it?'

She seemed a determined lass and I still didn't know what charms she had buried beneath her mass of clothing.

'Look, Anne-Marie, if I can do a swap around, I'll be at the Mission tonight. If I'm not there, you'll know why. I've only been at sea for five minutes, so to speak, and I'm not in a position to ask for favours, least of all from the Captain – he'd go bananas if I asked him if you could come on board, he's a strict disciplinarian as far as that's concerned.'

'Sounds like a real fun guy to me, Paul,' she added, with a shrug of her shoulders.

We parted in town; I was convinced that I'd just left my new acquaintance with a less than perfect impression.

'Sorry, Sixer.' That was the response I'd expected back on board the vessel because nobody wanted to change night duty arrangements. So that's that, I won't be seeing Anne-Marie again this trip, I thought, if ever again.

The evening dragged on, as duty nights on board frequently do, and as I half dozed on my settee, my thoughts were very much elsewhere.

'Sixer, where the hell are you?' A familiar voice reverberated down the alleyway.

'Coming, Chief.' I dashed to his cabin, half expecting some emergency had occurred in the engine room. 'Something the matter, Chief?' I enquired.

'Yes, Sixer, I think we could say that. There's someone here, just at the moment in my bathroom, who has apparently been on the quay for the past half-hour waiting to see you.'

She emerged from the Chief's loo looking not a little relieved and without her outer clothing, about half the size I'd imagined.

'Do you know this young woman, Sixer?'

'Anne-Marie, Chief.'

I quickly related how we had met and what had transpired – at least, most of it.

'Laddie, you've got a lot to learn. For a start, you don't treat the fair sex in the way they are accustomed to by allowing them to stand on the quay in this weather to freeze.'

'Chief, I told her that I'd make it if I could, but I didn't because I couldn't.'

It took just a few moments for the Chief to work out the logic behind my excuse.

'Laddie, you didn't ask me, did you? I am the Chief Engineer, in case it's slipped your memory. There's at least two hours left before the dance is due to finish, so get your glad rags on sharpish and be off with you before I change my mind.'

Where the taxi came from I wasn't sure but as we scrambled on board, Annie-Marie couldn't wait to enthuse over the Chief's generous gesture and, for once, I couldn't disagree. However, of one thing I was almost certain: the Chief's kind gesture was not solely motivated by his concern for my personal welfare, there had to be more behind it than just that. There was, but that wasn't going to emerge until we started carrying passengers.

'Can't wait to see your buddies' faces, Paul, when we enter the dance hall. They'll think you've abandoned ship.'

What was bothering me more was how good a dancer she really was and I was very soon going to find out. The trouble was that most of the people present were propping up the bar, leaving just a bit too much room on the dance floor for my liking.

'Anne-Marie, I can't dance until I've had a few drinks. Just can't get my act together.'

'Paul, for heaven's sake.' She grabbed me once again and before I realised it, we'd joined the Grand Prix circuit; the music, the lights and the bodies flashed by.

'Please, Paul, slow down. It's like dancing with a man with five legs. We're not trying to break the world land speed record. Does a few drinks slow you down?'

'I wouldn't like to guarantee that but I could give it a try.'

As we mercifully refreshed our respective parts with the local brew, one of the local lads invited her to dance and promptly set about showing me what it was all about. Sick with envy, I slunk to the sidelines. Then the doors opened and in walked all our engineers, apart from the Chief. They headed straight for the bar, looking as if they needed hot toddies. They didn't notice me at first but no sooner had they reached their destination than the music stopped, Anne-Marie spotted me and came over – they stared with undisguised amazement at my presence.

'Excuse me, Annie-Marie, I shan't be long.' I beat a retreat to the gents.

'Now then, Sixer,' the Second Engineer's voice thundered in my ears. 'Has thee eloped, gone off thy rocker, absconded or gone mad?'

'Well, Sec, it wasn't my idea. I've only been here about half an hour – got my marching orders from the Chief.'

The Second Engineer wasn't impressed by my pleadings. 'The Chief doing a duty night on board? You'll be telling me that pigs can fly, next.'

'Look, Sec, I'll go straight back to the ship but would you just explain to that blonde lass you saw me with why I've gone.'

'You can certainly be sure of that, Sixer,' growled the Second.

I slipped out of the Mission by a side door, wishing to hell that I'd never come to sea, not even really noticing just how cold it was. After ten minutes or so, I was under no illusion, I was very much beginning to regret choosing to try and walk back in such bitterly cold conditions, no traffic, nobody around, just the stark outline of the dock cranes in the distance. My groins ached as if I had double hernias each time I retrieved a foot from what seemed like bottomless crevasses with the virgin expanse of white never lessening. My whole body was starting to go numb and feelings of panic were flooding my thoughts. I could only think that drowning in a swamp could be worse and at least one didn't freeze to death.

'Keep going, for God's sake,' I kept repeating to myself as the distance to the ship gradually lessened, until the foot of the ship's gangway at last came within my grasp, or so I hoped. But the numbing cold had taken its toll, restricting all my movements, my head was aching as if I had been banging it against a brick wall, my lips wouldn't move, I couldn't speak. Must get up that gangway somehow, I thought, knowing that the last thing I would ever do was to fall into the Bay of Fundy.

Bit by bit I dragged myself upwards on my hands and knees and fell over the bulwarks onto the deep snow lying on the deck. Looking like the abominable snowman, I struggled into the accommodation, with nobody around to witness my plight. Staggering into my cabin with frozen hands, I couldn't even pour myself a glass of whisky. At least the Chief was not around to see the debacle. I couldn't help but think that even when I'd thawed out, that wouldn't be the end of the matter.

It wasn't, as I found out in the saloon at breakfast next day.

'Enjoy your night out then, Sixer?' The Chief winked as he called across the saloon from the Captain's table, obviously for the benefit of the Second Engineer and the others around him.

The Captain looked deadpan, the Second Engineer extremely puzzled and the others were wondering which night the Chief could be referring to.

I answered the Chief with a thumbs-up sign and thankfully he didn't pursue the matter.

I'd only just returned to my cabin when the Second Engineer appeared at the open door.

9

'Want to have a word with you, Sixer.'

'Yes, sure, Sec, come right in.'

'What was the Chief referring to about last night?'

I explained, as briefly as possible, the reasons for my unscheduled appearance at the Mission the night before.

'Why the hell didn't you tell me last night – don't say a word to the Chief about what happened.'

'Certainly not, Sec,' I replied. 'But I'd just like to know what Anne-Marie had to say when you told her I'd been ordered back to the ship.'

'Sixer, you'll learn that there's some questions you just don't ask, but for your benefit, I was reminded that Second Engineers have doubtful parentage, along with the rest of our breed.'

'Thanks, Sec, not to worry, I had a close squeak trying to get back to the ship.'

'That'll teach you a lesson then,' he added.

I wasn't sure what lesson he meant but I didn't argue.

Yet again on the homeward passage I was thanking my lucky stars that, apart from the odd headache, bad weather didn't upset me. One soon learns the good sense of the maxim one hand for the ship and one hand for yourself, particularly if the vessel is rolling and pitching at the same time, this being probably more significant in the engine room than anywhere else, especially with the 'up and downers' of the steam age, where the watch engineer is required to feel round the main engine, his hand making direct contact with the engine parts to make sure that they aren't overheating. It takes a steady hand, a cool head and both feet firmly planted in one place to carry out this exercise; no easy task when one is being corkscrewed in all directions simultaneously.

But it's in the bad weather conditions that you least want things to go wrong, and a good measure of self-discipline helps all round in order to try and ensure that the next watch doesn't inherit a load of problems.

I'd acquired a three-lens turret cine-camera not long before the start of my seagoing career and was hopeful that I could make a film on board to demonstrate what an engineer's duties were on watch and, much to my surprise, there was no shortage of volunteers to assist. The Third Engineer rigged up a portable lighting set, the Fourth Engineer offered his services as the 'star' of the epic and even the Chief almost got in on the act, although quite unintentionally by inadvertently gatecrashing a scene during filming.

A second surprise for me was when the film was developed; it surpassed my highest hopes and, in fact, was to be used in later years for pre-sea familiarisation courses at marine training colleges; hopefully it didn't put off too many potential candidates.

It was also a challenge to try and film bad weather conditions in particular heavy seas. This was no easy task because invariably the weather appearing on the silver screen never seemed as bad as it actually was. It never payed to be too adventurous with the camera in bad weather as it was asking for trouble in a big way. No camera, apart from underwater equipment, can withstand a sea water dousing. Nevertheless, my technique gradually developed, and I felt that a fair measure of success had been achieved if anyone had to rapidly exit the viewing room when watching one of my sequences.

'Sixer, we're apparently changing back to the summer trading pattern next trip and returning to the St Lawrence Seaway, so make sure you've got plenty of film. What you've seen up to now will pale into insignificance.' The Third Engineer was so pleased with his successful venture into film set lighting, there was no holding him back. Even the Fourth Engineer fancied his chances in a sequel but I had other ideas in mind for future ventures.

One of the disadvantages of being at sea is that one's girlfriends don't always appreciate the difficulties in trying to forecast when you will be returning home. I didn't have a steady girl at that time so it didn't seem necessary to me to try and maintain my home availability dates always at hand. The only trouble was that my poor mother often received telephone calls from girls she'd never even heard of who were trying to trace my whereabouts and when I was likely to be home next.

On returning home from this particular trip, my dear mum suggested that I should try and organise my social life on a less disruptive basis as far as she was concerned, or alternatively I get myself a steady girlfriend and keep in touch with her myself. Of course, I sympathised with her dilemma and assured her I'd try and come up with an answer before too long.

My father had hoped to train as an electrical engineer when a lad but circumstances, particularly the First World War, intervened and he eventually became a civil servant in the Ministry of Works, which brought him into close contact with the practicalities of life even if it was usually on remote and bleak aerodromes. He seemed to quite enjoy his son's new adventurous career and it was difficult to explain to him that there wasn't always a lot of adventure, in fact most of the time just the opposite.

Of course, all and sundry, including my girlfriends at home, had already decided that I had a girl in every port, which, at that moment in time, was absolutely true for no other reason than that Saint John was the only foreign port I had visited.

Whilst there was every possibility that Anne-Marie would not be consumed by despair at my failure to reappear in the not too distant future, I certainly would have liked the opportunity to share more time with her; but there was not the slightest possibility this would happen – a disappointment that was going to be repeated more than once in the future under similar circumstances.

3

This next voyage was certainly different to my first two; the weather was much kinder for a start, we were carrying a full complement of passengers and were certainly bound for the St Lawrence Seaway with Montreal, Three Rivers and Quebec included in our itinerary.

It turned out that many of our younger passengers were emigrating to Canada or the United States of America and were travelling by sea for the sole purpose of keeping their travel costs down. They were mainly travelling alone and were excited about what lay ahead. The voyage was an adventure in itself for many of them, in particular the younger single females, and it didn't take long for it to dawn on me that our Captain was not averse to a bit of adventure, provided it included the fairer sex – this despite his advancing years and his reputation as a strict disciplinarian with his crew.

The Third Engineer had him well summed up. 'Sixer, he's a lecherous old hypocrite, he's even got a load of etchings to try and justify inviting his chosen females to his cabin. He makes the Chief want to puke.'

'Really, Third,' I said. 'Very interesting indeed.'

The thought of crossing swords with the Old Man didn't fill me with enthusiasm but if I was going to make any headway with my social life on board, I was going to have to accept the challenge. Little did I know, at that point in time, that support for my efforts would come from unexpected sources, but I decided it would be better to let things take their own course. My thoughts turned to less contentious things.

As a youngster, one of my prize acquisitions was a cigarette card collection which had originally belonged to an uncle who had passed on. One of the sets that captured my imagination was the Canadian Outdoor collection; these cards were very colourfully illustrated and truly portrayed the magnificence and grandeur of the landscape, particularly the mountain areas, the St Lawrence Seaway and the Great Lakes.

Steaming up that very seaway for the very first time was quite uncanny. I definitely had the feeling that it wasn't the first time I'd been there, yet, of course, it certainly was. I've since wondered when folks talk about having the same uncanny feeling on visiting foreign parts they obviously know they haven't been to previously, whether or not they could have been influenced by having seen photographs or illustrations in their childhood.

The St Lawrence Seaway is more than just a marvel of nature, for Canada and the United States of America it's vital to their economy. Even the pilotage service for the ships is organised on an almost unique basis. To qualify, the pilots not only need to be expert ship handlers, particularly in passing manoeuvres at speed, but it also helps if they can fly an aircraft as well.

Each stage of the pilotage is so long that, to save time and maintain an availability of enough pilots, they fly themselves back to base after they have completed their own section of the Seaway. The skill they demonstrate in passing other vessels in close-quarter situations is quite phenomenal; in fact, my first experience of such a situation was in one of the narrower sections of the Seaway, which left me wondering how on earth we had been so lucky to avoid a collision. Whatever their remuneration was, in my humble opinion, these pilots certainly earned it.

'Sixer, this young lady would like a tour of the engine room, If you've time to lean on the rail to admire the view, then I'm sure you can spare some of it for such an admirable cause.'

'Certainly, Chief, I'd be delighted to do the honours.'

Taking note that the young lady in question was already suitably kitted out in a dazzling white boiler suit and a brand new pair of working gloves, obviously supplied by you-know-who, I led the way down below.

It didn't take more than a few words from Dawn to establish that she was an Australian and also emigrating. I couldn't help

14

saying to her that what she was doing seemed like taking coals to Newcastle but that remark fell on deaf ears, literally.

She thanked me profusely after we re-emerged from the engine room and, looking at her, I thought what a pity it was that there didn't appear to be much enthusiasm either among the opposite sex in particular or the marine authorities as a whole, to encourage females to try a seagoing career in one form or another, apart from being stewardesses.

'Paul, do you think it would be possible for me to have a look down a cargo hold before we arrive at Montreal? I might not get a chance when we arrive.'

It transpired she had a passion for sports cars, with the Austin Healey 3000 being her 'top of the pops,' and it just so happened that we had about 300 of them, all brand new, in a variety of colours, stowed in our No 3 hold.

'That, Dawn, is a most unusual request, if I might say so, and isn't a question I can answer simply, because the answer will have to come from the Deck Department.'

Ever willing to try and please, and after getting a special one-off permission from the Chief Officer, who also shared the Chief Engineer's dislike of the Old Man, I led the way down the ladders into the gloom of the chosen hold, at the same time pleading with her to hang on tight, vertical ladders being most unforgiving in the event of losing one's foothold or hand grip.

All the cars were unlocked and released from their securings by then, ready for discharge, and as I shone my torch over the gleaming array of automobile magic, Dawn suddenly decided she had one in her sights. After seating ourselves in her chosen car, she decided she would try out the gear change, but this proved a little less co-operative than she'd imagined.

I tried to assist from the passenger seat and, as our hands touched, she giggled, looking me straight in the eyes, then transferred her attention from the car's controls to mine. How frustrating, I thought, the Austin Healey 3000 may be fine for speed and road-holding but it certainly doesn't figure very high in the love-making stakes.

Dawn was obviously a girl not lacking in ingenuity and believed that where there was a will there was a way. Unfor-

15

tunately, just as things were starting to look promising, I had a feeling that were we not alone in the depths of the hold.

'Dawn,' I whispered in her ear, 'Don't look now, but if I'm not mistaken, there appears to be about half of the ship's company suddenly interested in a particular make of sports car.'

I kept myself out of direct view and slowly wound down the passenger window as carefully as I could. Then, gripping her hand tightly , I bellowed, 'Perverts' to one and all.

'That, Paul, says it all!'

One of the things to look forward to after the Western Ocean crossing was the Chief Engineer's safe arrival party and that night, after arriving and berthing at Montreal and after saying my fond farewells to Dawn, I got the surprise of my life about half an hour later, when who should step into the Chief's cabin but Dawn.

A bit of persuasion, also a slice of help from the Chief Steward and the Stewardess, and now, according to the Chief, she was in for the treat of a lifetime.

Apparently the party went with a real swing; unfortunately, and not for the last time, my drinks were tampered with ... the music was out of this world, my dancing took on new dynamism, Dawn was giggling like crazy ... then, as if by magic, the floor suddenly tilted about 45 degrees and I slid off the end of the world – with no parachute.

I awoke in my cabin next morning, almost naked, with a very cheeky note from Dawn leaving me reflecting on what might have been. I couldn't decide whether I was suffering most from an abused tummy, an extremely sore head or a deflated ego.

'You'll learn, Sixer, you'll learn,' was the Chief's reaction.

Whatever I was supposed to learn begged description, nevertheless I was hoping he would be right.

One of the problems of being a junior engineer was that of having to continually divide your working time between duties in the engine room and work on the deck machinery, mainly the cargo winches. This was certainly a major problem at times when the ship was in port, because it was only then that work on the main engines and boilers could be attempted safely but there was invariably insufficient time, so it was always a battle to get finished and the deck work became a pain in the proverbial.

The morning after the Chief Engineer's safe arrival party was no exception.

'Sixer, where the hell are you off to now?'

'Deck Department want the forward winches changed over to handle heavy lift cargo, Sec. Shan't be long.'

'But you only did the change round on those winches half an hour ago. What the hell are they playing at?' The Second Engineer was far from pleased with the Deck Department's continual demands concerning the cargo winches.

The Fifth Engineer and I had only been back in the engine room for about half an hour after our latest sortie on deck when a call came down below for both of us to present ourselves in his cabin.

'You know,' said the Second Engineer, 'I think there's a bloody vendetta going on,' as once again we disappeared, at the Chief's request this time.

'Oh, sod him,' said the Fifth, referring to the Second Engineer's impatience. 'What a ruddy lark this is at times, Paul, almost a joke.'

We knocked on the Chief's cabin door.

'Get your bodies in here pronto.' Our reaction was mutual, the Chief was not at all pleased about something which we were going to find out about now, right now. I hadn't seen him so upset and in such a state before.

'I have some bad new for you two. There's been a serious accident on the foredeck, a cargo derrick has just crashed down onto the number one hatch coaming. Fortunately the stevedores jumped clear and nobody has been injured, but the derrick is a write-off, according to what I've just been told by the Chief Officer. There is also apparently damage to the hatch coaming.'

The shock of hearing what had just occurred, and what could have occurred so easily if good fortune had not intervened, hit us both and my voice quavered when I asked the Chief what he thought had happened and, more importantly, what he thought we had or had not done to cause the accident.

'The most likely cause will have been the failure by one of you to make sure that the locking clips securing the clutch dogs for the

17

winch drive were properly tightened up, but until I've seen the various parts I can't be certain.' The Chief continued, 'What I need to know from you two and the Deck Department, is precisely when the gear was last changed over and by whom. 'You'd better get your thinking caps on. In the meantime, you'll both return to your engine room duties,' he added.

We departed with our tails, so to speak, well between our legs.

'Thank God nobody was killed or injured, Sixer. At least they can get us a new derrick and repair the hatch coaming.'

'That's true enough, Fiver, but we aren't going to be very popular with the superintendents. What gets me, though, is I'm sure neither of us would have forgotten to tighten those clips the Chief was talking about. In fact, come to think of it, I can't remember changing the gear over on the number one winches while either of us have been on the vessel.'

'You know, Paul, I think you could be right. Those winches have been in single gear for months, I'm sure, I'll check the deck gear logbook when we go down below.'

'Been on your holidays again?' asked the Second Engineer as we returned below. 'What's happened?'

The look on both our faces said it all. He didn't wait for an answer but shot straight up on deck to find out the worst.

Word spread quickly. The Third and Fourth Engineers sympathised with our position but had us both hung, drawn and quartered so to speak.

'Well at least they don't keelhaul you these days, Sixer.'

'Thanks, Third, that makes me feel a whole lot better.'

I was beginning to think that probably I'd had an almost too good a run of luck up to now, then the Second Engineer reappeared in the engine room and called the Fifth Engineer and myself over.

'Listen to what I have to say and don't interrupt me. The basic facts are, as you already know, the cargo derrick is now shaped like a banana so it definitely won't be doing any more cargo lifting but there isn't a great deal of damage to the hatch coaming, fortunately. But, more importantly from your point of view and no doubt you'll be relieved to hear, I am almost certain the accident happened because the securing clip had fractured and, due to this,

18

the dog clutch disengaged – not because the clip hadn't been tightened up.'

'How have you worked that out, Second?' asked the Fiver.

'Well, quite simply, the fracturing didn't happen today; in fact, judging from the rust on the fracture faces, it failed some time ago.'

'What does the Chief think, Sec.' I asked.

'He thinks now that the freezing cold weather and ice conditions on deck have probably either been the cause or at least been a major factor. He says that he is going to compile a report for the superintendents recommending that they change the material of the clips from cast iron to mild steel.'

'He'll be popular – that could cost a fortune when you think how many pairs of clips would need to be replaced if all of the ships require attention,' I added.

'That, Sixer, has bugger all to do with you, so if we can now suspend this little meeting, maybe we can get some work done before it goes out of fashion. Then, maybe, just maybe, I might consider giving you two a half-day before we sail.'

The Second's idea of half a day off did not necessarily mean that one would be lucky enough to get the whole afternoon ashore; in fact it was not until the middle of the afternoon that we headed off towards downtown Montreal with words of warning ringing in our ears about not hanging about in the dock area because of the hoodlum element.

'What's that lying in the gutter, Fiver?'

We'd just turned a corner on the edge of the dock estate and were emerging on what appeared to be the main road leading up to the city centre.

'If it's what I think it is, that's the first actual body I've seen,' he replied.

'Me too, and not a very pretty sight,' I added.

The road ahead rose quite steeply, which meant that we could not cover the ground as quickly as we would have liked to. We had no alternative, there was no other way, so we passed within feet of what certainly was a very dead male who had been brutally knifed.

Feeling sickened by what we had just seen and gasping for breath, we finally reached the top of the road, which fortunately did lead into the downtown area.

I was carrying my cine camera in its bag but it never occurred to me to shoot even a couple of feet, if only to place on record the gruesome scene of the crime, much to the relief of the Fifth Engineer, who told me later that if I had, he would have departed forthwith.

'What's going on here then, do you reckon, Paul?'

We'd moved on right into the heart of the business sector and were now looking down over a boundary fence towards a yawning chasm that stretched as far as the eye could see.

'Looks as if the ground has opened up and swallowed the buildings below.'

'No, Paul, it's a building development of some kind. You can see the excavators and bulldozers in the distance. They look like toys from here, don't they?'

We eventually found a gap in the fence and decided to take a closer look.

'Heh, you guys are late. Your buddies are already down there, the opening ceremony's due to start at any moment.'

The security officer, obviously fooled by our inquisitiveness and the camera gear, directed us towards a massive press gathering, all there to record the opening of the brand new Montreal underground rail system by the Prime Minister.

'Better get filming, Paul, or they will chuck us out.'

I soon found out that trying to film amongst a seething, struggling mass of media people was not for me. In fact, to save embarrassment all round, we decided to beat a hasty retreat and leave it to the professionals. I had no illusions about the challenges they faced in trying to record material just that bit better than their competitors, but that's what it must be all about, so good luck to them.

That wasn't going to be the last time I would unexpectedly stumble into an uninvited situation although it would be many months before history repeated itself.

Montreal struck us both as a city of many contrasts. Not least of all the architecture, with old buildings of beauty and charm, the modern buildings being equally impressive, particularly the hotels, and we decided we should try, next time we were there, to see a lot more and get a real taste of the place.

One of the few disadvantages of being single and unattached at sea sometimes is the scarcity of mail addressed to you, just the occasional letter from one's relatives and maybe a girlfriend who's genuinely missing you. Nothing to compare with the volumes normally received by one's married compatriots at each port.

But this voyage things were different because of a break-in at our Montreal agent's offices. Our mail was missing and it made me feel a whole lot better not to be the only one deprived of news from the home front.

We had expected to be sailing upriver to Quebec, but for reasons that we were not told about this did not happen, which meant that the Quebec mail did not reach us before we departed, so there was even more justification for the married crew members to feel deprived.

Homeward bound and not long after we left Montreal with a full complement of passengers, the Chief once again summoned me to his cabin.

'Sixer, the Captain has told me that he is not prepared to put up with your frolics with the female passengers any longer and that I must warn you that unless you refrain, he will ban you from the public areas of the vessel, with you having to eat all your meals in the mess room.'

'Oh, right, Chief,' was about all I could think of in reply.

'Right, what do you mean, right, Sixer?'

This was no good at all, the Chief was definitely getting all worked up again and in a lather. His enmity for the Captain was once more rearing its ugly head. I was beginning to wish I was a married man and not a bachelor who was proving to be a convenient weapon for him to fight his personal battles with.

'Look, laddie, there's one young lady who I'm pretty certain is showing a definite keenness to know more about you, so I shall have to speak a few chosen words in her delicate ear and, who knows, your dreams may be answered.'

'Thanks, Chief, it's really great that you take such an interest in my personal welfare.'

'Do I detect a touch of regret in your voice, Sixer? For heaven's sake, just be sensible, don't go wandering around the passenger accommodation, then you've nothing to be concerned about.'

But before the Chief had an opportunity to put his plan into action, I was punished from above, so to speak, which left me wondering whether the Captain had divine powers as well.

Despite being aware of the dangers of anything that's hinged swinging around violently in bad weather, I unfortunately had a memory lapse when I was next on watch. Whilst I was climbing down the vertical ladders at the top of the boiler room, the vessel was pitching fairly heavily and, just as the top of my head was about to descend below the level of the hinged access grating, the wretched thing swung down like a hammer blow ... my head, stars ... then complete darkness.

'Hell, Sixer, are you okay?'

The fireman on watch below hadn't been aware of what had happened to me. Then he thought a can of red paint had upturned itself and was dripping down onto him. On losing consciousness, I'd fallen down a few rungs of the first section of the ladder onto the grating below.

'Just a gash, I think, and a bloody awful headache,' I replied. 'But I had better go up topside for a check-up. Pass on that info to the Third Engineer please.'

My pride was severely dented, even more than my head. How could I have been so foolish to get caught out in the way I had?

The headache and blurred vision persisted until we reached the UK, so I escaped the attentions of one and all, including the Captain, with the Chief accepting that I was not in good running order certainly for entertaining the opposite sex.

At least it looked as if my career in the Merchant Navy would survive a little longer, but I had a feeling that the Chief would once again require my personal involvement in his vendetta plans on the next voyage.

4

We sailed again on 28 May 1960 with the weather almost perfect, the Western Ocean being like the proverbial millpond.

There'd been no change in the ship's complement. The Captain had hoped to be relieved in order to take his long overdue leave but, to his annoyance, this had not happened. The only patience he could spare was for his precious passengers with the Mate and Second Mate having to bear the brunt of his bad temper, although the Chief Steward didn't entirely escape being on the receiving end when the occasion arose.

I decided to give the saloon a miss at meal times so as to try and avoid any trouble with the Deck Department.

Then the Second Engineer decided it was time to test, once again, all the emergency gear.

'Sixer, I want to see the starboard aft lifeboat engine running. You know what to do by now, you should be able to manage on your own.'

'Hi, there.' A youngish-sounding female voice took me by surprise. 'Are we going to have to abandon ship?'

'Oh heavens no, nothing like that, just routine testing to make sure all's well,' I replied.

'What's wrong with everybody on this ship?' she continued. 'Anybody would think us passengers were lepers. Only the Captain's talking to us. I've told him what he can do with his what's-its – he's a dirty old man,' she continued.

'Well, first things first. I'm Paul, your humble Sixth Engineer, who also happens to be the Captain's least favourite flavour of the month simply for doing precisely what I am now, talking to you. I wouldn't mind if I was committing some cardinal sin or was breaking all of the company's rules, but all I've done, according to those who know him better than I do, is make him bloody jealous.'

She laughed. 'My name is Anne and I can see I'm going to get you into more trouble if I don't disappear right now.' She was looking upwards towards the bridge.

I glanced round, saw the Old Man glowering in my direction and dived for cover under the lifeboat.

'See you later,' she added, and then disappeared.

'Good lad,' said the Second. 'We'll make an engineer out of you yet.'

The lifeboat engine had fortunately decided to co-operate for once when I swung the starting handle.

'Thanks, Sec, I'm sure you will, but sometimes I think I won't be around long enough for that to happen.'

I recounted what had happened just before he arrived on the scene.

'Sixer, the Chief will be well pleased, she'll certainly be invited to his safe arrival party.'

'That's just great, Sec. The Old Man will have a field day if he catches me red-handed with her.'

'For heaven's sake, Sixer, you're getting paranoid about him. Have faith in the Chief – he can fix most things, or so he thinks.'

Maybe, I thought, but definitely not the Old Man. After all, he was one of the most senior masters in the company and had seen a lot of wartime service in both the Western Ocean and the Baltic. He was undoubtedly an oil-and-water man if ever there was one, engineers being a breed he'd rather not have to share his vessel with and only tolerated because they were a necessary evil. At least we weren't far from the North American coast, and Anne and the other passengers would be leaving us. Maybe divine providence would intervene and we'd be blessed with a party of nuns as our homeward-bound passengers.

I'd just come off watch and was sitting in my cabin sipping a cold drink, trying to cool off a bit before having a shower.

'Who's that?' I said, hearing a faint tap on my cabin door.

'Only me,' she replied. 'Are you decent? Just wanted a quick word to let you know the latest'.

'You'll get me shot, Anne. Come in, but please keep it brief before the Old Man's spies reveal your whereabouts to him.'

'You're not going to believe this but the Captain asked me to accompany him to the passenger lounge and then, if you please, started lecturing me about his promiscuous officers who caused him a great deal of anguish. Guess who he nominated as the most promiscuous of the lot?'

'I can guess,' I replied. 'Chance would be a fine thing, Anne; if you believe that, I'm afraid you'd believe anything.'

'Your Chief has invited me to his party when we berth .'

A cheeky grin lit up her face and with that she was gone. Probably that was just as well otherwise I might even have mentioned my less than perfect performance at his last party.

Whether or not Anne had a sneaking suspicion that there was more than an element of truth in the Captain's lecture, I didn't really know. She was obviously determined to spread her charms around the gathered throng as the Chief generously extended his hospitality to one and all. Despite his blatant attempts to lace her drinks, I got the impression that nothing likely to cause the Old Man any concern was about to happen. At least I would be able to turn to next morning, hopefully not feeling like death warmed up, a mouth tasting like a cesspit and a headache of monumental proportions.

'A charming girl, Sixer, very, very nice indeed but not your type,' was the Chief's comment next day.

'Too good for me, you mean, Chief.'

'Never mind, Sixer, your time will come, even if I have to personally arrange it.'

I couldn't help but think that, under different circumstances, I would have been delighted, even honoured, by the Chief's concern for my lack of social success. But feelings of trepidation were never far from my mind when I thought of the likely consequences if the Captain took it upon himself to intervene.

One of the Fifth Engineer's ambitions in life was to have a look around a television studio and broadcasting centre. He'd previously discovered that the Canadian Broadcasting Corporation had main studios in Montreal, so when the Second Engineer decided we'd done enough hard graft to earn a proper half-day off, the Fifth Engineer suggested that we should present ourselves on their doorstep and request a guided tour.

'Don't you think that's asking a bit much?' I offered in reply. 'Surely they'll require an advance warning.'

'Nothing ventured, nothing gained,' retorted the Fifth, and so be it, we ventured forth.

'Here we go then, Paul,' he proclaimed as we entered the reception area. 'Leave the talking to me,' he added.

The reaction we received, even to this day, still amazes me. You would have thought we were VIPs. Of course we could look round and they would provide a guide to explain everything. There would be a delay of about a quarter of an hour while our tour was arranged, so probably it would be a good idea to help ourselves to a coffee, take a seat and relax.

'See what I mean?' chirped the Fifth. 'Just needs a bit of charm and a lot of cheek.'

'I wonder if they'd have been as keen to offer their hospitality if they'd known that we're just a couple of sailors off a ship in port,' I replied.

'Who knows, Paul, but they're not going to find out unless, of course, you decide to tell them.'

What followed was truly a spectacle of action, vision and sound, the like of which neither of us had experienced before. Our guide led us on an amazing trail, we crept through 'live' studios and control rooms, seeing recorded programmes in the making and several going out live at that moment on separate channels on the national network.

'Either of you two ever read a news bulletin?' our guide enquired.

'No,' I said, 'I can't claim to have done that. How about you, Alan?'

I fully expected the Fifth to proclaim that his vocation back home was just that but, surprisingly enough, he simply accepted the challenge, after being reassured that there was no intention to broadcast his efforts.

To be honest, the Fifth looked quite distinguished for his rela-

26

tively young age – probably it was his neatly trimmed goatee beard and carefully combed dark hair, combined with an immaculate pinstriped black suit, that did the trick. I was very much the minder, so to speak.

Although he fluffed the pronunciation of several words on the news script, nevertheless the recorded result was not too bad at all, although unlikely to attract any offers of employment.

'Your turn now, Paul.' He was determined to let me experience the pressures of the hot seat.

'I am not suitably dressed to appear before the cameras, Alan,' I insisted.

He didn't argue about that and we continued our tour, our guide proving to be a fund of knowledge despite his relatively youthful appearance.

Whilst naturally we didn't expect the ladies' loos to be included on the itinerary, we were little surprised to be ushered past a studio identified as the Tele-cine Department, our guide quietly advising us that no visitors were allowed inside this studio as this was the corporation's policy, with no explanation forthcoming.

Our tour was finally concluded with refreshments in the entertainment suite. We expressed our heartfelt gratitude to our host, who'd given us a real treat.

'You know, Alan, I still find it hard to believe that we were allowed to penetrate so deep into their organisation without having to prove who we were.'

'For heaven's sake, Paul, if you really must know, the vessel's agents cleared the way for us.'

'You mean they did know all the time that we were off a ship?' I enquired.

'I haven't a clue, but does it really matter?' The Fifth had other things on his mind. 'Paul, why do you think they wouldn't let us have a look in the Tele-cine Studio?'

'Goodness knows, they've probably got some specialist equipment in there they're testing or developing which they don't want the world to know about.'

Little did either of us realise that in all probability what they were hiding from us was the earliest form of video recording and transmitting equipment.

27

Back on board, when we recounted our experiences, the general immediate reaction from our shipmates was total disbelief with suggestions that we had concocted the whole thing in order to cover up for other more likely misadventures. Our biggest regret was that neither of us had thought of asking for a memento of our visit. This omission was considered to be too unbelievable to be acceptable, therefore only the Fifth Engineer and myself knew better.

The Second Engineer decided, after we arrived at Quebec, that there wouldn't be sufficient time to start any maintenance work because of the limited time we would be spending there with very little cargo to be worked. He therefore decided that the Fifth and myself could be spared for yet another half-day.

Naturally enough, and because of the warmth and the generosity of the hospitality that had been offered to us both in Montreal, we couldn't wait to test the water here, so to speak, as well. But if either of us had had the slightest idea of what was to unfold ashore in Quebec, we certainly wouldn't have been in such a hurry to get ashore in the first place.

After hearing so much about the area, our main objective was to see the Heights of Abraham, particularly as Canada's history is so much linked to this landmark. To help us get there we decided to take a horse-drawn landau in the manner advertised in all the local brochures.

We joined a relatively short queue of tourists waiting at the landau rank. Despite waiting for what seemed to be an eternity, we were not getting any closer to boarding a landau. The Fifth Engineer's patience finally deserted him and he demanded to know why we were being overlooked. I did manage a GCE in French but unfortunately this didn't equip me to even begin to understand the obvious torrent of abuse that was pouring out of the landau driver's mouth.

'You know, Alan,' I said, 'This guy's not being at all friendly, in fact I'm pretty sure he hates your guts and probably mine as well.'

'Because we are British, no doubt,' he replied. 'Sod him, come on, we'll walk.'

'You must be joking, those bloody horses earn every scrap of food they get hauling these landaus up there.'

28

But the Fifth wasn't going to be defeated, so off we went on the long upwards haul. Not unexpectedly we didn't make it. The Heights of Abraham remained a distant vista.

'You know, Paul,' the Fifth had been in deep thought for longer than normal. 'That sodding landau driver has obviously never forgiven the English for defeating his French general on those wretched heights. Didn't that prevent them from establishing Canada as a French colony?'

'I'm not sure whether your recollection of the historical events is quite right, but if that is what actually happened, then all I can say is I wouldn't like to meet our friend down some dark alleyway one night in downtown Quebec,' I added for good measure.

5

'Homeward bound again, Sixer,' announced the Chief. 'According to the Chief Steward, the Captain has told him to make sure that a certain young lady passenger is seated next to him at his table. Apparently she's extremely attractive and Irish as well. This time you'll play your cards right or so help me God.' He wasn't joking.

'That sounds like a threat and a promise, Chief, if not in that order.' I tried to sound whimsical but with little conviction.

'We'll see, Sixer, we'll see,' he added.

I still wasn't certain how I figured in the Chief's estimation as an engineer but he certainly seemed convinced that I could deliver the goods, as it were, in his personal vendetta with the Old Man. Being the only single officer on board the ship seemed, at first, to be a tremendous advantage when it came to getting involved with the opposite sex, but the combination of my singular lack of success to date and the threats from the Old Man if I did score, were not doing my ego or reputation any good at all.

My, my, I certainly could see why the Old Man had made sure of his strategic advantage at the outset. She was stunningly attractive, truly an Irish colleen. The warmth of her personality lifted us all and, not only that, she had a sharp mind with a cripplingly funny sense of humour. I watched, totally captivated from my vantage point two tables distant from hers in the saloon.

'You know, Sixer, you are a bloody embarrassment,' said the Second Mate. 'Can't you take your eyes off the Irish attraction, anybody would think you'd never seen a beautiful girl before.'

'Not at all, Peter but you've got to admit she's almost too good

30

to be true; not only that, but that lecherous old sod upstairs will be doing his best to procure her charms.'

'I'm sure you're right, but I can tell you this, Paul – if you don't stop treading on the Old Man's toes, you'll be getting your marching orders and maybe more.'

Prophetic words from the Second Mate.

'Peter, don't you appreciate I'm in an impossible situation. You know only too well how the Chief views the Old Man's attempts to win over any attractive female who steps on board this ship. I'm considered a more suitable candidate to do the winning over by the Chief, and let's face it, Peter, what a bloody waste of talent. It's no good, I'm afraid the Chief expects me to do his duty, so help me God.'

'Well, all I can say is, I wouldn't like to be in your shoes if the Old Man decides to do his worst.'

'But surely you can't be sacked for doing a spot of entertaining if the lady is agreeable?' I pleaded.

'That,' replied the Second Mate, 'Depends on the entertainment being offered and who's taking part. If it included the Old Man and excluded you, then no doubt no one would get the sack.'

I valued the Second Mate's opinion. It struck me that he was a good judge of character and circumstances. He had me more than a little concerned.

'How's it going then, Sixer,' enquired the Chief next day.

'Fine, Chief, just fine,' I replied, with my tongue in my cheek.

'Really, that's not what I've heard, the Second tells me you're not really trying.'

'Well, you know how it is, Chief, don't want to force myself on her. She seems totally infatuated with the Old Man.'

Oh dear, oh dear, I had just said the entirely wrong thing.

'Absolute bloody nonsense, never heard so much rubbish in my life.' The Chief was nearly apoplectic. 'You, you just aren't trying.' He decided it was time to issue threats. 'How about a stretch of daywork on top of your watches until the end of the voyage?'

Then he mellowed.

'I know you aren't the flavour of the month with the Old Man, but Sixer, let me put it this way, if you don't get your finger out soon, my patience will be finally exhausted. Do I make myself clear?'

I couldn't win. 'Perfectly Chief, perfectly,' I groaned.

How exactly his instructions to me concerning what I should do with my finger were going to help, I could not for the life of me see, but in for a penny, in for a pound. There was no way that I had any intention of flogging my guts out on daywork even if it meant an early demise to my seagoing career. I was totally puzzled about what motivated the Chief to be in constant battle socially with the Captain but I decided that discretion was the better part of valour and didn't probe too deeply into the matter.

'Could I just have a few words with you in the games room, please?'

My opening gambit took her a little off guard. I'd appeared at the saloon door as she departed after lunch; I was due back on watch and was already late but she followed me.

'I'm Paul, the Sixth Engineer. Sorry I haven't introduced myself earlier but, for reasons I'll tell you about shortly, I have to choose my opportunity very carefully and it's never seemed to occur until now. Anyway, much more important, I'm madly jealous of anyone on this ship who grabs your attention. I think you are absolutely captivating and I can't take my eyes off you, you know.'

'Well, Paul, after all that, what can I say? I'm just simply Oona who'd noticed your eyes were constantly giving me the once-over, yet I was coming to the conclusion I must have the dreaded lurgy because that's as far as you seemed to be interested.' She was smiling broadly with not even a hint of bitterness or criticism in her voice.

'Oona, any attempt by me on this ship to socialise with the opposite sex is totally frowned upon by the Captain. That might only seem to you to be a small problem but for me it's worse than the dreaded lurgy.'

'I know,' she replied. 'I asked the stewardess what was wrong with all the officers and she fully enlightened me about your Captain and his medieval ideas. Anyway, don't worry too much about me, I've come across his type more times than you would probably believe. He's quite charming really and absolutely harmless, old enough to be my grandfather – well nearly.'

32

'Really,' I replied, acutely conscious of my sudden loss of suitable words to respond in an appropriate manner. 'We could have a coffee later but if I don't get back on watch now, I'll be in trouble from that direction as well.'

'Yes, that's fine, Paul. I'll look forward to that.' I then departed faster than the proverbial flash in the pan!

'Sixer, where the hell have you been?'

The Third Engineer didn't share the Chief's enthusiasm to see the Old Man suffering with his amorous adventures.

'Sorry, Third,' I replied. 'Won't happen again.'

'Next thing, you'll be wanting to change watches to improve your availability,' he added.

Once again, I couldn't help but think that chance would be a fine thing.

Two days later, just when I thought that the Chief was letting things ride, so to speak, he raised the matter once again as I handed the logbooks in.

'You're certainly not the fastest mover on two legs, Sixer, but I understand things are steadily improving. Is that right?'

I decided, this time, that honesty might inflict a less destructive blow to my ego.

'Not exactly, Chief,' I said. 'The Old Man seems to keep her well occupied when I'm off watch, so our meetings are few and far between.'

'Right, that's it, enough said, Sixer. You'll be changing watches with the Fiver because you're going to have a party, invite the other passengers and the off watch officers. The ball will then be in your court so don't clout it out of the ground or kick it into touch,' he added for good measure.

The Chief's attempts to put my likely reactions to his grand plan into a sporting context didn't strike me as being in the best of taste, but he hadn't finished yet. He stared ahead then slowly nodded his head, turning to look me straight in the eyes.

'Don't let me down this time, Sixer.'

So that was it, the grand plan. How could I be so lucky to have a Chief Engineer who was determined to make my social life on board not only challenging but decidedly dodgy career-wise, with no guarantee of any reward whatsoever for all the risks taken.

The grand plan envisaged me being totally free of watchkeeping from 1800 hours one day until 0600 hours on the next day. In order to achieve this happy situation, I would be required to be on watch for six hours instead of the usual four on the afternoon before the party, and for two hours only on the morning after. In return for this, the Fiver would do the exact opposite but with the added inducement of an additional watch off which I would do for him later.

My first thought, as usual, after coming off watch was to get a shower, but on opening my cabin door I just stared in disbelief. All I could think of was that Oona was due to visit me any minute and there was no way that she should see what had just been presented to me, not on a plate but all over the cabin walls and other places as well, no doubt.

'The bloody so and so's, how could they do this to me? I bet the Chief's behind this.'

'Talking to yourself, Paul? Don't they say that's a sign of madness,' she joked.

It was Oona, of course, just a little early.

'Hi there, nice to see you. I am not at all sure you'll be laughing when you see how my cabin has been decorated unless you have a perverted sense of humour.' I tried to stay calm but only with great difficulty.

'My, my, very artistic tendencies,' she murmured as she gazed about her. 'You don't look the type, but life's full of its little surprises,' and she then winked in the way only a woman can.

'I can certainly assure you, Oona, these creations certainly did not spring from my hand and they'll definitely have vanished over the horizon come this evening. Changing subjects, do you think they'll all turn up?'

'I've no idea at all, but for your sake I hope they do, otherwise you won't have a party atmosphere. That reminds me, one of the girls says she won't come unless the Second Officer is there and another one mentioned the Fourth Engineer.'

'I'll do my persuasive best, but no guarantees, Oona. Sorry for the visual assault,' I added, referring to the uninvited artistic adornments to my cabin which could only be likened to a sexually frustrated kangaroo having been let loose with tins of pastel colours but no paintbrush.

She pressed her fingers against my lips. 'Say no more, somebody's gone to a lot of trouble on your behalf even if it is a bit misplaced, to say the least.'

I was just beginning to think that for once everything was swinging nicely into place, a cabin full of happy-go-lucky people, good music on tape, plenty to drink, with a few snacks rifled from the passenger lounge and it was only early evening.

Then there was an unmistakable type of knock on the cabin door. In fact there were two knocks only but they sent my alarm bells ringing; oh hell no, was all I could think. My pulse raced; what now?

It was the Chief Steward. 'Sorry to disturb your fun, Sixer, but there's a message from the Captain for Oona. He requests her attendance for drinks with his guests.'

'Should have guessed. I'll tell her,' I replied.

'You'd better go, Oona, otherwise the Old Man will be inviting me up next, but not for drinks with his guests.'

Fortunately, she didn't argue.

'Don't get upset, Paul. I'll be back later — that's a promise.' With that she was gone.

Yes, I thought, and pigs will fly, not a cat in hell's chance that I'll see her again this evening.

They came and they went, I filled glasses as and when required, changed the tapes and tried to pretend that life hadn't, once again, managed to deal me a poor hand.

By midnight, they'd all gone. They'd thanked me for a great party and had enjoyed themselves very much; it was just as well they hadn't bothered to ask me if I'd had a good time.

It wasn't just a feeling of being a little upset, more like a sickening frustration. What a fiasco. The Chief will be dumbfounded. Well, bunk, here I come. I unbuttoned and unzipped my outer garments, then there was a tap, tap on my cabin door, then again. What the hell now? I was just about to shout 'Get lost,' or words to that effect, when a distinctly familiar female voice whispered, 'It's only me, but for heaven's sake hurry up and open the door, please Paul.'

Surprise, bewilderment, action – move yourself, James, I was pleading with myself.

'Hell, no!' I exclaimed as I fell flat on my face, tripping over my momentarily forgotten floored trousers.

My head hit the door, which released the safety catch; the door burst inwards under the influence of Oona's encouragement and on top of me she fell.

'Sorry,' we said in unison.

I struggled free and got the door shut and locked. If she hadn't giggled uncontrollably, I'd have probably felt a whole lot better.

'Paul, have you got no shame? I'm not used to male front nudity – for heaven's sake make yourself decent.'

'I didn't rehearse that little act, you know. If I had I probably wouldn't be ending up with a king-size bump on my forehead.'

'I've said sorry once. If that isn't enough or you're sorry I've come back, I'll go right away,' she added.

'Hey, no, of course not, it's just that you took me completely by surprise. Look, let me get you a drink if there's any left. Then I'll sort myself out.'

We sat on my settee, a drink each to hand. The music helped. We held hands and looked into one another's eyes. But the question and answer time was not over yet.

'Paul, tell me, would I be right in thinking that your Chief is no friend of the Captain? In fact it almost seems as if he bears him a grudge.'

'You're a very perceptive girl, Oona. Sometime I'll tell you a lot more about it but surely you haven't come back to hear me talk about those two individuals.'

'No that's true,' she said. 'I'd like to know more about you. You intrigue me, you seem genuinely interested in me as a person and aren't just chasing me for my looks.'

'True enough,' I replied. 'But first, tell me what is a beautiful young Irish girl doing returning from North America? I would have thought that once there, you'd have stayed, met your Prince Charming and lived happily ever after.'

'Sometimes things don't work out the way you plan.'

I listened, fascinated, as her tale unfolded, warming to her delightful Irish brogue, her dazzling beauty, her exquisite

36

aroma and her physical softness, which I longed to touch and hold.

She was born in Galway Bay, one of six children, and her parents, being devout Catholics, not unsurprisingly frowned on their youngest daughter's ambition to work in North America. Her determination to escape to what she thought would be even greener pastures than her native land had transported her first to the United States then on to Canada, to work as a waitress, a croupier, a hotel receptionist and finally as a children's nanny in Vancouver.

'You know, they seemed such a lovely family. There were three children, two girls and one boy, their mother was a teacher and their father a theatre set designer. They had everything that money could buy, everything that I had dreamt of as a child, a beautiful home in the mountains above Vancouver and at first, everything seemed absolutely perfect. I got on well with the children and their mum, in fact the kids adored me. I certainly didn't notice anything wrong with their mum and dad's relationship. Then, over a period of time, it gradually dawned on me that there was no relationship at all between them. It transpired that he had established a homosexual relationship with some queer in the same theatre. His wife was truly broken-hearted when she found out. Finally, after trying desperately to win his love back and losing, she attempted to end her life. Fortunately I just found her in time and the doctors at the City Hospital, saved her life. I couldn't take any more, so I handed in my notice. To be honest, I feel very guilty leaving three broken-hearted kids and a mother on the edge of suicide but I decided to come to England to stay with my sister who lives in Coventry and think things over before I make up my mind what to do next.'

'My life has had its fair share of ups and downs to date but, thank God, I haven't had to try and cope with such horrid circumstances as you've obviously had to face. You know, I reckon there's nothing particularly wrong in men loving men, and likewise with women, provided they don't clamber into bed to perform acts that, quite naturally, must stink to high heaven in all senses of the word. Absolutely bloody revolting, if you ask me. When you think about it, if God had intended that men or women perform sexually with their own sex, he'd have designed them a whole lot differently. It strikes me as very strange that apart from the odd exception, most animals have no difficulty in making up their minds which sex they belong to.'

'Paul, please don't misunderstand me but I didn't come back to receive a lecture in morality, no matter how strongly you obviously feel about it. Anyway, who knows, I could be wrong, you might be one,' she added in a teasing and provocative manner with a look in her eyes that certainly told me she definitely wasn't.

'No, Oona, I might be a bit slow off the mark but that's just me. Better have a fill-up before I change my mind!'

'Ha, ha, funny as well,' she responded. 'But strictly not peculiar.'

We both laughed, suddenly smothering each other with kisses as if they were going out of fashion.

'I'm just beginning to think you know when you are wanted,' she whispered in my ear. She convinced me that my cabin door wasn't about to open unexpectedly and the Old Man appear in person, no evacuation of the vessel was imminent, no fire alarms would disturb our amorous entanglements and, of course, they didn't . . .

'Could I be right in thinking, Sixer, that at last, we're one up on the Deck Department?'

Judging from the Chief's confident tone and beaming smile, he knew more about the previous few hours than either Oona or myself. I wickedly felt like telling him another woeful tale but refrained, deciding life was worth living once again.

'Yes, Chief, Oona and I really hit it off.'

'Really,' said the Chief, 'And you survived, but then times have changed since my days.'

We both laughed, me with a sense of relief having, at last, achieved what was expected of me in my line of duty.

'Good lad,' he added. 'Keep it up.'

'Yes, certainly, Chief, I'll do my very best, my very best. As long as you don't tell me I'm no longer hard up.'

That produced another bellow of laughter which was like music to my ears but as I joined the Chief with tears rolling down my cheeks, I wondered just how much longer I would survive the Old Man's wrath.

I didn't have long to find out. The next day the Chief called me to his cabin after I came off watch.

'Sixer, I have been instructed by the Captain to tell you that you are banned forthwith from all parts of the vessel above main deck level at all times, the only exception being for emergencies.'

'Oh, then there can't be much doubt that my days on this vessel are numbered, Chief,' I replied. It was hardly surprising that the Old Man had reacted in the way he had but nevertheless I was deeply concerned that my extra-mural activities would reach the wrong ears and have dire consequences for my seagoing career.

'You must be due for some leave by now, Sixer. I'll speak to the Superintendent when we get back and ask him to arrange for you to be relieved. Nothing to get steamed up about,' he added in a manner intended to reassure me.

I didn't exactly share the Chief's apparent lack of concern about my future. How many black marks had I scored and would they follow me through my career? At least those in the know on board the vessel thought I'd had a raw deal from the Old Man. Oona threatened to do some very nasty things with his wretched etchings but, thankfully, decided that discretion would be the better part of valour.

Little did I suspect that fate might quickly intervene to redress the injustice I felt that I had received.

Unfortunately for the Captain, he couldn't have chosen a worse time to dress down the whole of the Catering Department, including the Chief Steward, but, there again, he probably hadn't realised that within 24 hours, we were going to run into some extremely heavy weather. During this type of weather, in addition to raising the table edge boundary restraints, the dining saloon stewards usually wet the table cloths to discourage the table ware and cutlery from chasing each other around.

On the day in question, the vessel was pitching really heavily into head seas as we took our seats for lunch. The Chief Engineer and the Chief Officer took their seats in their usual places opposite one another, next to the Old Man at the top of the table; a few passengers who had decided to brave the elements sat down the sides and the Second Engineer and the Second Mate sat facing one another at the other end of the table. I sat at my usual place at a

39

side table with other junior officers as the stewards served the soup course.

Quite suddenly, not unexpectedly but still catching just about everybody out, the vessel took an enormous nosedive and immediately two rows of newly filled soup dishes raced each other down the Captain's table, each determined to be the first to deposit their piping hot contents onto his lap. Only the Second Engineer had managed to grab his dish before it took off, but as the vessel again repeated the same manoeuvre even more violently than before, he let go his dish, muttering under his breath about not being selfish.

I vacated the saloon as fast as my legs and the ship's motion would allow. My sides were nearly splitting and as I reached my cabin, I collapsed in a heap on the floor, convulsed with laughter. All I could visualise was the Old Man's face, his expression truly revealing his innermost thoughts, unwinding with a rapidity more reminiscent of an old hand-wound movie ... shock, incredulity, yelp, yelp, as the scalding hot soup found its mark, almost a giggle to regain his composure, more pain, then apparently, after my hurried departure, anger as he wreaked vengeance on all and sundry for the calamity that had befallen him.

One of the younger passengers reckoned it was the funniest sight she had ever seen in her whole life and was well worth all the extreme discomfort she'd had to endure from the bad weather.

The ramifications for the Catering Department were far-reaching: they were charged with gross dereliction of duty, having failed to dampen the tablecloths before positioning the soup dishes. Each guilty party ended up with a DR (Decline to Report) endorsement in their discharge books for their pains and the Captain's.

The remaining part of the voyage was, for me, a question of almost solitary confinement wondering what was happening to Oona. Probably the Old Man was now redressing the balance very much in his favour but I hardly dared show my face above the parapets for fear of crossing swords once again with him.

The Chief seemed to lose all interest in my goings-on with the opposite sex, which, if nothing else, tended to confirm what I'd always believed – he was really only interested in seeing the Old Man bite the dust with his amorous adventures.

It was the stewardess who mentioned Oona for the first time since the party night.

'Paul, you know she does feel quite guilty about what's happened to you. On top of that, she's bothered about how she's going to get to her sister's home in Coventry. Can't you have a word with her and set her mind at rest? She won't talk to me about it.'

'I'd love to, Jean, but you tell me where we can have a chat without the Old Man knowing, and don't say in the linen locker, if you please.'

'I know it's difficult, but he has to sleep sometime and when he has his head down next, I'll ask Oona to pop down and see you.'

It didn't take too long to work out that Oona's problem was simply related to a lack of ready cash to enable her to purchase a rail ticket, so I offered to hire a car and drive her to Coventry.

'You don't have to, you know, but if you don't mind, then I would be very grateful and delighted.'

For one of the first times in my life, I was not looking forward to the future. The moment of parting was surely getting closer; neither of us wanted it to happen but we were helpless to prevent it.

The last days of the voyage were mixed with joy, sadness and regret but it was only when we were finally seated side by side in my hire car on the road to her sister's that my heart yearned to backtrack to the beginning of our homeward voyage. The last hours we spent together in Coventry remain etched in my memory for ever, the final parting of two people who'd fallen in love but were not prepared to admit it to each other, for all the wrong reasons.

The final wave ... the choking lump in my throat ... grab the steering wheel ... foot hard down and get to hell out of here as quickly as possible ... don't look back.

41

6

It had seemed an eternity since signing off articles on 30 June, the *Libra* being now just a memory from the past.

Back home for a spell, trying to re-establish contact with my friends and realising that they and I were seeing life from entirely different perspectives. They were getting married and starting families, I still had a long way to go before trying to join their bandwagon, or so it seemed to my dear mum.

The relieving duties in port were beginning to become more than a little monotonous and just when I was resigning myself to believing, despite the Chief Engineer's assurances to the contrary, I had done my future career no good at all on the *Libra*, I was summoned to the Superintendent's office to be told that I was being promoted to Fifth Engineer to sail on the *Aquila*. I would be signing on articles on 15 October for a voyage that would take me to the Middle East and beyond.

Before we even sailed from Birkenhead, I'd managed to survive a very realistic fire training course organised by the Liverpool Fire Brigade for Merchant Navy personnel, our Sixth Engineer got himself arrested on board by the police and then on the last night before our departure, I managed to find yet another girl in a million.

But, as they say, first things first. My initial enthusiasm for the trip took a definite nosedive when I discovered that the Second Engineer, with whom I'd be watchkeeping, carried a larger-than-life chip on his shoulder. Apparently, despite all his efforts, he just could not pass the next level of examinations which would have ensured his promotion to Chief Engineer and he had great difficulty in resigning himself to the prospect of having to remain a Second Engineer as long as he stayed in the Merchant Navy. His reputation for wreaking vengeance on junior engineers who dared to even hint at his problems was well established and, as time would tell, his ability to blame everyone else but himself for his shortcomings didn't lead to a harmonious relationship on the work front nor, for that matter, after working hours either.

At first, though, his bark seemed worse than his bite, so to speak, but then, after being given our marching orders to attend the fire training course full-time for nearly a week, the Sixth Engineer and I changed our opinion when the Second decided that in order to make up for lost time due to our absence, we'd both have to work out of watch hours on daywork, once the vessel had sailed.

It soon became obvious that the fire training course was not going to be a holiday either. The Liverpool Fire Brigade were also carrying a chip on their shoulders about how they managed to capsize and sink an *Empress* liner in the Gladstone Dock when trying to extinguish a devastating fire.

It was apparently no mere coincidence that their recently appointed Chief Fire Officer was previously a Merchant Navy chief engineer. The course lecturer, bless his soul, had sometime previously decided to take it on himself to warn unsuspecting trainees not to try and make clever remarks about the brigade's apparent difficulty in failing to realise that ships tend to capsize if you go on pouring water ad infinitum on board – that is, if they valued their sanity.

The Chief Fire Officer had apparently developed an uncanny habit of managing to get himself into a lecture room unnoticed and, just as an unsuspecting trainee felt the need to raise a laugh, the 'fire axe' would fall on the trainee, leaving him in no doubt whatsoever, that the Chief not only knew what he was talking about but would have the trainee's guts for garters if he persisted with his cheek!

As it turned out, the warnings were heeded but on the third day, when we thought all was going well, the opportunity arose to prove to ourselves that we were less than perfect.

'Right, lads, you've had enough of the theory, now it's time to see if you can put it into practice. You're going to pass through a wall of fire. You'll be suitably equipped with protective clothing, breathing apparatus and water hoses, but before that and to familiarise yourself with smoke conditions, we'll let you have a taste of our smoke chamber, wearing a smoke helmet.'

The course lecturer went on to explain to us the use of the hand bellows that supplies air to the helmet, which, he emphasised, must be operated continuously whilst the helmet was being worn. He then explained that we would be working in pairs, taking it in turns to wear the helmet then operate the bellows.

'You also have a lifeline, lads, and I'll now explain the signalling system with the line which you must stick to,' he continued.

Naturally, I'd expected the Sixth Engineer would be partnering me, but that was not to be,

'Right James, your turn now.'

Suitably equipped, feeling just a little apprehensive but with the adrenalin flowing, I ventured forth, apparently receiving a goodly supply of air to breathe. Grasping the lifeline knowing my life could depend on it and trying to follow the strict orders to keep moving along and out of the opposite side of the chamber, all at first seemed well. Then on reaching what seemed to be the densest smoke, I couldn't move any further. There didn't appear to be any more air line, then my air supply stopped. I tugged like fury on the lifeline, demanding air but with no response. Absolutely brilliant, I thought; can't go on, not sure of the way back and no air to breathe.

I was about to find out how one's natural instinct for survival knows no bounds. Within seconds, I'd surfaced in frantic disarray, my bellows partner having believed, so he said, that I was already out of the chamber.

All right mate, I thought, two can play that game; you can have a taste of the same medicine, see if you enjoy the sinking feeling and panic when one tries to breathe without an air supply. But because we were running late, the lucky devil got let off the hook as we each donned the gear for the real thing.

It's quite surprising how confident one can feel wearing the latest fire-protection gear and self-contained breathing apparatus, charging forth with one's colleagues and aiming the powerful spray nozzle at the seat of the fire, extinguishing the fire as if by magic and emerging unscathed.

A feeling of justified pride was quite evident amongst my

colleagues as we later collected our certificates for completing the course successfully, and when the Sixth Engineer and I returned to the vessel, we just hoped that our success would at least convince the Second Engineer that our absence had all been worthwhile.

For the Sixth Engineer, it wasn't really going to matter either way as it subsequently turned out.

I heard their voices first then there were a couple of rapid knocks on the Sixth Engineer's cabin door.

'Police officers, please open your door.' I heard the Sixer jump in surprise and a loud crash as his chair fell over.

'Are you James Alan Moore?'

'Yes, why?' His voice had a distinct waver and certainly no ring of confidence.

'We have a warrant for your arrest and require you to accompany us to the local police station in connection with your failure to make maintenance payments to your wife and support your children...'

It was 6.15 a.m., the morning after we had completed our fire training course. At first when I heard their voices, I thought I was still asleep having some nightmare, but then the reality struck me, I was awake and these coppers were not on a social visit. Even as I stood at my open door, shock and disbelief at what was happening made me feel both angry and sick at heart.

'Nothing to do with you, young man, so just keep yourself out of the way, if you don't mind, please.' One of the officers had obviously detected my concern about what was happening.

'I'm sorry, officer, but I don't quite see it that way,' I continued unabated. 'You don't have the right to come on board this vessel without even informing the Captain, or the Chief Engineer for that matter, what you're here about. Then to walk off with the Sixth Engineer before those officers are aware of what's going on.'

'Right, young man, I did warn you to keep your nose out of matters that don't concern you. What's your name and rank?'

I answered and he wrote the details in his notebook.

'I'll give you five seconds to withdraw what you just said

45

and apologise to us, otherwise I'll be arresting you for trying to frustrate the arrest of your colleague.'

Needless to say, it didn't take me that long to do the necessary and I disappeared into my cabin like a scalded cat feeling as if the KGB had infiltrated our legal system.

To be perfectly honest, nobody on board the vessel knew about the circumstances that had brought the visit of the law and caused the Sixer's arrest. All we knew was that he was a young married man with two young children and that things hadn't worked out at all well for him concerning his marriage. It was only much later that we found out he had stopped paying maintenance because his wife had started an affair with a so-called friend shortly after he commenced his seagoing career, and this had resulted in a separation.

The law, as usual, was not interested in the rights or wrongs of the case and we all felt a great deal of sympathy for the Sixer when more came to be known about the circumstances.

Neither the Chief or the Second Engineer had the slightest intention of taking the vessel to sea without a replacement engineer. Next day, the new Sixth Engineer arrived on board in a bit of a stew, having just joined the company and as green as they come. He'd hardly had chance to gather his wits together and pack his bags, and it was obvious to all as he stepped on board that he was also very bemused by all that had suddenly and unexpectedly happened to him.

I felt that a little basic timely advice might help him to avoid crossing swords with the Second Engineer prematurely.

'Sixer, the Second Engineer can be a bit more than a pain in the backside at times. He doesn't suffer fools gladly so, for heaven's sake, listen very carefully to what he has to say and try and carry out his orders as best you can. You'll be on watch with the Third Engineer. He's OK but all I can say is that you're going to have to be a fast learner.'

'I've repaired ships during my apprenticeship, Fiver, but I haven't a clue about running them. I'm not at all happy about being thrown in at the deep end.'

'Well,' I said, 'There's not much you can do about that, but they know it's your first trip so they shouldn't expect too much from you.'

That evening, before we sailed, the Second Engineer accepted the Fourth Engineer's voluntary offer to be the night on-board duty engineer so the rest of us could have a final night ashore.

We headed for New Brighton in the firm belief that this was the right direction to go to have a great final fling. Whilst walking between watering holes, purely by chance, we came across a car with its bonnet up and an exceedingly attractive young lady peering despairingly into the engine compartment.

'Trouble?' I volunteered.

'Yes, you could say that,' she replied. 'I'm supposed to be meeting friends in Birkenhead about now.'

'Fiver, over here please.' The Third Engineer had moved on and beckoned me. I joined him.

'Paul, you're surely not going to get involved here. Hell's bells, it's our last night. We can call the AA, they'll fix the problem for her.'

'Dave, I know that, but if you two want to press on that's OK by me. If you're stopping off in the pub just up the road there, I'll join you there. Shouldn't be too long.'

I returned to the lady in distress.

'You don't have to bother, you know. I couldn't help but overhear what your friend was saying. Sounds as if you're condemned men, either that or you must be going away.'

'Well, I'm Paul and I'm pleased to say none of us are condemned men, at least not in the way I take it you mean. But we are sailing tomorrow, so it's our last night ashore for longer than I care to think about.'

'If this isn't too much of a coincidence, my name is Paula. We ought to get our act together,' she joked. 'At least we wouldn't need to change our names, would we?'

Chance would be a fine thing, I thought, but here I was, about to sail off into the far yonder and with a beautiful girl inviting me to join her, at least for a bit of fun. I decided to keep my thoughts firmly focused on her car.

'First things first, Paula. I'm no garage mechanic, but the battery seems to be all right, you've got plenty of petrol so I'll have a quick look in the distributor.'

How the points had been operating at all was a mystery. A bad

case of arcing, to say the least. A box of matches had to be pur-
loined from a passer-by, then, as if by magic at least as far as she
was concerned, the engine burst into life.

'Oh, Paul, you're a marvel.'

'Not really. Just a bit of luck, which I never seem to have when I
break down.'

'Look,' she said, 'I feel rotten at having to dash off now but I've
promised to meet my friends. I'll see if they will come back with
me. If you stay at the pub up the road with your friends, I could be
back in about an hour. Then we could have a party. How about that
then?'

'Sounds fine to me, Paula. See you later then.'

Typical, I thought, as she drove off into the night. Why couldn't
it have happened a few days ago, not on the night before our
departure?

I headed into the Crooked Billet and found them not the least bit
surprised by my solo appearance.

'Fiver, you'd no chance there, way above your level. That's
what I was trying to say before you got involved.' The Third
Engineer had the situation well weighed up, or so he thought.

'Thanks a lot, Dave, but just for once you could be wrong,
although I shan't know for another hour or so.'

I quickly briefed them on my stroke of luck in fixing her car for
her.

The thought possibly of Paula returning with a carload of beau-
ties had crossed my mind, but not what the Third Engineer had to
say next.

'You know, Paul, in my experience lovely-looking girls often
have ogres as girlfriends, and if that turns out to be the case then I
shall do my famous disappearing act.' The Third Engineer continued, 'You've suddenly gone very quiet, Sixer. What will you do if
we are inundated with ogres?'

It seemed to me the Sixer had not seen too much of an adventurous life to date. He was probably more concerned about not getting involved in any antics which could result in him missing his
ship on his very first trip.

Time dragged on. No sign of Paula or any of her friends.

'Didn't I try and warn you, Paul. I'll buy a last round before closing time and then it's back to the ship for me and no doubt you too, Sixer.'

I was feeling decidedly deflated. Probably I'd misjudged her; certainly wouldn't be the first time I could be held guilty of dropping such a clanger.

'OK then,' I said. 'Let's be on our way.'

Back on board, I sat in my cabin thinking about what might have been and feeling not a little sorry for myself.

Next morning it was an early turn-to to prepare for sailing. Emerging from the engine room for breakfast, I was accosted by the Chief Engineer.

'Fiver, there's a female on the quay asking for you, by the sound of it.' He didn't seem at all pleased. Junior engineers were becoming more than a pain in the neck to him. 'Five minutes, mind you, and then back on board.'

'OK, Chief, I'll just see who it is.'

'Paula, how on earth did you trace me here?'

'Well, as you are the only ship that's sailing from Birkenhead today, that wasn't too difficult. You certainly are surprised to see me, aren't you?'

'Naturally. What happened last night, then?'

'Well, I didn't like to say anything last night to hurt your feelings because you were so kind. Actually I fibbed when I said I was going to meet some friends. I was on my way to meet my boyfriend and I didn't think you would want to share an evening with him. Anyway, I've come back now to thank you again and apologise for not coming back last night. I just wish we had met earlier.'

'Paula, that's just how I feel as well. Anyway, thanks for making the effort and coming now. Quite honestly, I feel like a condemned man having to say goodbye but I've got to go now. Take care of yourself, lots of luck.'

All I could think was that all these shenanigans were not doing me any good at all.

I tried a wry smile as I reboarded the vessel. Did I detect a few tears as I glanced at her upturned face? Of course she knew, just as I did, that we would, more than likely, never meet again on the face of this earth.

7

The first few days of any deep-sea voyage are usually tense while one adjusts to the seagoing routine again and, on this occasion, also getting to know one's new shipmates. The tenseness can easily become unbearable if the sea conditions are rough and your shipmates are not the ones you'd have chosen, if you'd had the chance.

We steamed out of Birkenhead into the teeth of a severe gale and it was very obvious that the new Sixth Engineer was no sailor. His suffering soon laid him low.

'Richard, you'll have to pull yourself together,' I said, coming off watch the first evening outward. 'This weather could be with us for several days and you could probably adjust to it if you give yourself a chance.'

'Easy for you to say,' he replied. 'I've never felt so rotten in my life. I'll try and get back on watch as soon as I can.'

Fortunately the bad weather did not agree all that well with the Second Engineer either so he tended to remain in his cabin most of the time when off watch.

In fact the bad weather persisted right through the Bay of Biscay, down the Portuguese coast and only eased when we passed through the Straits of Gibraltar into the Mediterranean when, as if by magic, the clouds lifted, the sun burst forth, the sea looked as if it had been dyed pastel blue and the air temperature rose to 75 degrees.

'Right, you two lazy buggers,' bawled the Second Engineer next morning. 'It's time you started earning your living. Straight after breakfast I want you both on deck overhauling the cargo winches, OK?'

We nodded our understanding. There was no doubt in either of our minds that the Second was determined to have his pound of flesh, come what may.

'He talks about overhauling the winches, Paul. That's the understatement of the year – if you ask me, they need rebuilding.'

'That could well be the case but we're in no position to argue,' I replied.

On the second morning on deck, the relative peace and calm around us was suddenly shattered by the roar of aircraft engines. We dived for cover, thinking the worst, as an aircraft almost clipped the top of our masts with its wings before banking steeply to make a return pass.

'It's a ruddy fighter, Sixer. For God's sake, run for it and get under cover,' I shouted.

We both took off like bats out of hell and literally dived into the amidship accommodation, waiting for the expected gunfire, breathless.

The aircraft repeated the manoeuvre once again but still there was no gunfire.

'Come on, Sixer, let's get back on deck before you-know-who accuses us of malingering.'

The Third Mate appeared on deck.

'The Captain has sent me down to tell you to ignore these aircraft in future. They're French Air Force planes based in North Africa supposedly checking for illegal arms shipments, but in fact use any vessel steaming along the coast as target practice – simulated, that is,' he quickly added.

'Well, let's hope they've got simulated bullets in their guns in case they decide to press the firing buttons,' I added sarcastically.

By the time we had reached the eastern end of the Mediterranean Sea and were proceeding towards the Suez Canal, we'd almost completed our labours on the foredeck machinery but that still left a fair amount of work to do on the aft deck machinery.

Whilst we were steaming down the Mediterranean and although we were fairly close to the coastline, there wasn't much to see except for the mountains of Algeria. The temperature had risen steadily but, being November, was never uncomfortably hot or humid.

'We anchor at Port Said to join the convoy going south down the Canal,' explained the Second Mate. 'The northbound traffic has to wait in lay-bys for us to pass.'

It also transpired that the engine room watches were required to be doubled for the duration of the Canal transit. This meant that I joined the Fourth Engineer on the Chief's watch, and the Sixth Engineer together with the Third Engineer joined the Second Engineer on his watch, the watches each being of six hours' duration.

Before we departed from Port Said, I tried to film the local scene but was firmly stopped in my tracks by a port official who was obviously very sensitive about any record being made which might get into the wrong hands. During the Canal transit, I had a little bit more success by making sure my camera was kept out of sight of any uniformed official.

As ever, the pilots demonstrated their remarkable dexterity despite not knowing the particular handling characteristics of the vessels they are called upon to manoeuvre.

With the sea temperature rising, so did the humidity; a breath of fresh air was becoming a sparse commodity especially when you had to share it with a ship's company that had grown to twice its original size.

'Who are all these ruddy passengers we're carrying?' I asked the Third Mate. 'Seem like a bunch of Egyptian gypsies, they don't do anything useful and no doubt would end up looting your cabin if you left your door open.'

'I don't know about that, Paul,' he said. 'But you're right, they are only needed when ships are going northbound for handling the mooring ropes in the lay-bys, so they get a free ride southbound.'

We weren't sorry to complete the Canal passage, and even the prospect of having to turn to on deck after watches to continue our efforts with the winches didn't seem too bad compared with the six on, six off, watch procedure for the Canal.

When it became obvious to the Second Engineer that there wouldn't be sufficient time for the Sixer and myself to complete the work on the winches before we reached the first discharging port, Aden, he decided we'd have to be taken off watch duties, to give us the full working day on deck.

'Just as well we didn't break our backs before Suez.'

'You must be joking, Richard. We've got our work more than cut out even now to finish before we reach Aden.'

The Fourth Engineer was getting more than a little envious of our daywork hours and the Third Engineer was decidedly disgruntled at having to do his watch on his own, particularly as the daytime engine room temperature, he told us, was around 128 degrees and the sea temperature around 95 degrees. We certainly didn't venture down below out of curiosity, to find out.

The problem with working on deck during daylight hours in the temperatures we were experiencing was the blisteringly hot deck plating, which made one's toes curl up, and whilst that discomfort was bad enough, the totally unexpected arrival of a winged spectator nearly made me require a change of underwear.

'Don't move,' shouted the Sixer. 'It's near your right shoulder.'

Not only were my toes curling, I felt my hair rising. 'What's near my bloody shoulder, Sixer? I croaked.

'To be honest, Paul, I don't know, but it's bloody big, ugly and has got massive wings.'

That was enough for me. I took off ... without wings. Loud guffaws of laughter rang in my ears from the aft deck.

'Haven't you seen a locust before, Fiver? Mind you, I've never seen one that size before.' An able seaman was giving me the benefit of his superior experience.

'That a locust?' I muttered. I felt a complete idiot. 'I thought they flew in swarms.'

'They do, that's why they're such bloody big swarms,' he added, roaring with laughter.

That evening, over our usual drinks, I admitted to the Sixer that one of the few things I really disliked in the non-human species was large winged insects.

'All I can say to that, Paul, is that if that wretched locust had landed on me, I'd probably have had a heart attack.'

Aden was almost on the horizon as we completed our labours on the winches.

'No doubt, Sixer, the Second will have some cynical comment

to make about our timing and how we just managed to get the work done in time, dodging engine room watches and the like.'

But surprisingly enough, he didn't. It looked as if the heat was getting to him and sapping his mental processes.

The bustle of the Canal passage was about to pale into insignificance as the vessel moored at buoys in the Aden harbour, which is no postage stamp size of water space. Within 15 minutes of being moored, there wasn't a single area of deck space left; we were overwhelmed by a seething mass of humanity, all more than anxious to sell anything and everything, including their souls, if that was necessary to put money into their pockets. The boat deck had been transformed into an oriental open market, the vendors plying their exotic wares and bargaining, with their lives apparently depending on the outcome. Anything and everything from carpets to TV sets was on display, all undeniably excellent value for money provided one didn't have to pay import duty on returning to the UK.

The winches appeared to be performing reasonably well but then the speed of cargo discharging was certainly not going to break any records, so they weren't really being tested.

I hesitated about buying myself a radio; I reckoned it would probably break down the moment we steamed out of Aden, to be ever a reminder of my folly in giving in to temptation, and in the end I resisted. The opportunity to get ashore at Aden just didn't arise and, after what seemed an eternity, we were on our way, heading across the Indian Ocean bound for our next port, Karachi, the main port of Pakistan.

As we left Aden, I couldn't help but think that the biggest problem for the ship's navigators was avoiding the numerous dhows that appeared as if from nowhere. They didn't show any navigation lights, therefore all one could presume was that those on board were oblivious to the dangers of night-time collisions.

At least the weather remained clear but the night-time temperatures didn't drop as much as I would have liked.

Not long after leaving Aden our first serious problems in the engine room since leaving the UK made their uncomfortable presences felt. Our main boilers were soon generating more smoke than steam, which is certainly not conducive to enabling the vessel to continue at normal speed. The Second Engineer initially accused the Sixer and myself of not operating the boiler smoke tube soot-blower equipment properly, a procedure whereby steam at full boiler pressure is directed through the fire tube banks to blast soot and combustion products up the funnel and prevent blockages.

Despite our combined efforts, it was becoming increasingly obvious that we were not winning the battle, particularly with the port forward boiler, and a shutdown of this boiler became inevitable. No sooner had this been done when a further shutdown, this time of the starboard forward boiler, was ordered by the Chief Engineer.

'If this problem turns out to be due to negligence by you and the Sixer, I can assure you you'll both be for the high jump.' The Chief was far from being a happy man. The vessel's speed had had to be considerably reduced and the Chief was incurring the Captain's wrath accordingly. Whether there would be sufficient time to cure the problems with the boilers at Karachi, was also worrying the Chief.

Arrival at Karachi couldn't come quickly enough for the engineering department. The preliminary investigations showed that the fault lay with the equipment and not with the operation of it by us two accused engineers, much to the Sixer's and my relief. For the technically minded, the internal parts within the housing were not extending and hardly revolving at all, fortunately easily resolved by fitting replacement spare parts we had in our stores.

A swarm of boiler cleaners descended into the boiler room on the morning of our arrival and after feverish activity and much to the surprise of us all, the work was completed, the boilers were closed up and tested, eventually, to the satisfaction of the Chief.

Whether it was sheer relief at not finding anything more seriously wrong, we didn't know, but to our mutual surprise, the Second Engineer granted the Sixer and myself shore leave that afternoon.

'Come on, Richard, grab your camera and let's be off before he changes his mind or something else goes wrong,' I said.

As we walked down the road towards the dock gates, passing carts being pulled by a weird variety of animals with not a horse in sight, neither of us had a clue where we were heading. Would we last out in the stifling heat? Our shirts were clinging to our backs like wet rags, the soles of our feet were already baking from the heat of the road surface – we might as well have been bare-footed.

'I know what you must be thinking, but we might not get another chance to venture forth here. Apart from that, any chance to get away from our mutual tormentor is not to be sneezed at,' I exclaimed.

Walking out of the dock gates, we were immediately accosted by a bike vendor, complete with stall.

'A do-it-yourself taxi rank, Richard. What do you reckon? I haven't ridden a bike for years.'

We both agreed that anything that would get our feet off that sizzling hot tarmac had to be good news, and for what seemed a remarkably cheap hire price, we clambered aboard our respective two-wheelers and set forth in the general direction of the city.

After a short while, neither of us were sure whether or not we were riding on the correct side of the road.

'Well, it's not a one-way street, that's for sure, Paul. But nobody seems to be bothered which side of the road they use. We'll stick to the left-hand side and hope for the best, don't you reckon?'

'Guess so, but I've never seen anything like this in my life before.' And I hadn't.

As we neared the centre of the city, the words 'traffic density' took on a new meaning for me. Literally anything and everything that could move, regardless of the number of legs or wheels attached or the condition they were in, seemed present.

'Ye gods, Paul, we'll never survive in this melee. Talk about every man for himself, it looks as if that goes for the donkeys, mules, elephants, asses and the rest.'

We jumped off our bikes before we were mown down and parked them against a bridge parapet. The skyline looked at first like many another capital city, an amalgam of skyscrapers, tower blocks and the occasional truly outstanding example of architec-tural beauty. At second glance and at closer range, a flag of British origin fluttered on a building, looking not a little incongruous in the circumstances.

'Possibly the British Residents Club or something similar,' was the Sixer's comment.

As I recorded the scene on film he interrupted me.

'Come over here, just look at that lot, have you seen anything like it in your whole life?' He was leaning over the parapet of the bridge on which we had stopped. I joined him and stared down at a scene of abject poverty, with the most dilapidated tin huts imaginable.

'No drinking water, no sanitation, no privacy. How on earth do families survive in these conditions? Yet look at the washing hanging there – it looks clean enough. We don't know how lucky we are in the West.'

'I'd like to bet you, Paul, that our compatriots over there don't give a monkeys.'

'I wouldn't know about that, but I doubt if it would make the slightest bit of difference if they did,' I replied.

'I tell you what, if pigs were kept in those conditions in Britain, those responsible would be had up for cruelty,' Richard added.

'Come on,' I said. 'Let's press on, there must be better things to see than this.'

But as we rode away from the scene, I knew that a permanently lasting image had been implanted in my memory of that unbelievably contrasting scene. I only hoped that I'd accurately recorded on film the true pathos of what we had just seen.

We continued on our travels towards the city centre and came across what must have been the mother and father of all traffic jams. It all appeared to be contrived by somewhat splendidly costumed policemen, wearing headgear to match and looking for all the world as if they were conducting the Hallé Orchestra from their dazzling white rostrums using their equally dazzling batons.

Once again we jumped off our bikes; this was too good to miss.

'I must try and capture a little of this, Richard. How about taking a short walk down that sidewalk?' I was pointing to where there was a gathering of vendors. 'I'll continue shooting over there after filming the fun and games on this junction.'

By now he'd learnt not to argue with me about appearing on film and opted for the easier course of simply doing what

I'd asked. The traffic policemen did not let me down either; in fact, it could be clearly seen from their actions that they were revelling in their moment of stardom. Not so the poor Sixer. He had his beard trimmed, his shoes shined, was offered every service under the sun and some that weren't, and after refusing tempting and unrepeatable offers, he decided he'd had enough and went on strike.

'No more, thanks, Paul. Let's get back on our bikes and be away before I'm further tempted,' he pleaded.

We cycled on, trying to stay alive and not get run down by every conceivable form of transport.

'Look at that bus over there,' I shouted. 'Looks like standing room but only on the roof, if you please.'

One couldn't help but be impressed by the relative calmness and fortitude of the populace. It didn't seem to bother them in the slightest that the bus they were travelling in was significantly overloaded and not safe to be on the road. Their only consideration seemed to be that the vehicle had wheels and they turned, therefore there was a reasonable chance that they would be taken from A to B.

We came across some quite impressive buildings and stopped to take a closer look. They turned out to be the national TV and radio broadcasting studio headquarters, and when I was just about to expose a few more feet of film, I was pounced upon again by a uniformed officer of the law who had literally sprung from nowhere. No, I could not record this scene and if we didn't move on, we'd be leaving with him but without my camera and film.

'What the hell is wrong with these countries, Richard? They're so sensitive about taking a paltry bit of film of their buildings. Anyone would think we had designs on blowing them up,' I added.

'Well, that could be the reason, I suppose. They don't have a clue who we are and they don't bother to ask.'

I couldn't help but think that a few monetary notes in the right place and at the right time would have convinced our uniformed friends that they had nothing to fear from us, but I didn't feel inclined to test the idea out.

Arriving back at the dock gate and after handing back our bikes in one piece, thankfully, we reflected on our little adventure and concluded it had been worthwhile, even if a bit frustrating, trying, worrying and a little upsetting at times, but not necessarily all in that order.

8

We were on passage from Karachi to Bombay. The weather was as hot and humid as ever, with the only relief available from these conditions being a shower and a cold beer, hopefully afterwards.

'I must try and write home before we reach Bombay. I haven't put pen to paper since we left the UK. What's today's date? My calendar has done a walkabout.'

'Twenty-seventh November in the not so good year of 1960, Richard.'

We'd been talking to one another on deck and as I returned to my cabin, the sounds reaching my ears reminded me once again that the Second Engineer was obtaining his relief in his customary manner from his tape recorder: extremely loud bursts of opera, which reverberated down the alleyways to the dismay of the majority of the rest of us. The only solace for us was the thought that while he was listening to his chosen music, he was not inflicting more misery on us down below or on deck.

I couldn't help but reflect on my previous voyages and compare life on the *Aquila* with that on the *Libra*. A totally different existence, barely any amusement, jokes being as rare as the proverbial rocking horse business, with not even the hint of the feminine touch because, having no passengers, we didn't even carry a stewardess.

Thoughts about the lovely lasses who had so fleetingly but indelibly passed into and out of my life, combined with the efforts of the Chief to ensure I received the Distinguished Service Medal for valour in the course of pursuing his vendetta against the Old Man, were never far from my mind. There certainly wasn't going to be any repeat of this scenario on the present voyage.

Then, just as if to press the point home and right out of the blue, the dreaded lurgy struck me, or at least my intestines. From feeling just sticky and uncomfortable most of the time, acute pain and discomfort riddled my abdomen. I quickly became exhausted rushing up the engine room ladders in time to make it to the toilet, my insides having apparently decided to put on an outward show of strength. How many times could I repeat this before I collapsed in a heap?

What a state to be in, was all I could mutter to myself as Bombay came into view. I just about summed up enough strength to point my camera in the general direction of the shoreline and fire away before I returned to my cabin to await the arrival of the doctor.

Not surprisingly, he diagnosed dysentery. Then he did surprise me. Out of his case he produced what appeared at first sight, to be mini-submarines but were obviously his answer to my illness. One could see the logic about prescribing these weapons; if they didn't succeed in choking you when you tried to swallow them, they would lodge, hopefully, in the lower bowel region, creating a total blockage allowing nothing to escape. In the state I was, I would gladly have swallowed the boxful.

After only a day of this wonder medication, there was a marked improvement in my health and I gradually began to feel like a human being again.

'Right, Fiver, you've had your holiday break now, let's see some action sharpish like. I want you and the Sixer to make sure that soot-blower equipment is still performing properly, so get to it right now.'

We did. No way were we going to be accused of letting the side down again. Down below, boiler cleaners were busy but they didn't have the nightmare to face that their counterparts in Karachi had dealt with. We laboured away, and to our relief found that the equipment we'd been instructed to deal with was in good working order.

Our reward was another half-day off, and the Sixer and I disappeared ashore as quickly as possible before minds were changed. Once on terra firma, we made our way towards the Seamen's Mission, hoping to find out what was the best way of getting around this vast city.

61

The ravens, as ever, were making their presence felt, diving and swooping over the ships and sheds, beggars of the air, missing nothing that resembled food and avoiding the rest. But it was the beggars on the ground that almost broke our hearts. Young children, both girls and boys, many half-naked and all barefoot, deliberately maimed solely for the purpose of persuading the better-off to part with a few rupees, supposedly to help them survive but more likely providing sustenance to others more capable of doing the providing.

We'd been warned that if we showed the slightest generosity towards them, we'd be mobbed. They hung around the dock areas hoping for more than sympathy from the seafarers the world over. I could see the Sixer reaching into his pocket. 'Richard, if you do, they'll probably make it impossible for us to leave the mission and we'll simply end up back on the ship. At least leave it until we're on our way back, they're bound to be still around.'

We entered the mission, a different world, the clambering and reaching arms and hands behind us thankfully on the other side of the doors. A very welcome coolness wrapped itself around us as we descended some steps in the half light.

A gentle voice from behind offered even more reassurance. 'Gentlemen, can I help you. I'm the mission hostess.'

We turned to gaze admiringly at probably the most beautiful young lady I'd ever seen. She had large half-smiling eyes and was dark-haired, dark-skinned, slender and extremely alluring, very aware of her effect on the opposite sex but, at the same time, not inviting the slightest comment or overture.

We explained our requirements and were given a mass of information and advice. Drinks then ensued, of a non-alcoholic nature but very cool and welcome.

After offering our grateful thanks, we set forth. We strolled along the Marine Drive wondering how soon it would be before someone would get knocked down by the speeding traffic crossing a very busy road junction.

'Look at that guy sleeping on the pavement underneath the seat,' said Richard.

'Probably recovering from crossing the road,' I added.

The heat was making one want to try and find some shade but

there wasn't enough time to slacken our pace. We were just thinking about hailing a taxi when we ourselves were hailed by an
earnest young man, smartly dressed and obviously not slow at
coming forward.

'You like girls?' he asked almost demanding an answer.

'Here we go, Richard.' I turned to the Sixer. 'If I'm not mistaken, we're about to be made an offer we can't refuse.'

Our young friend persisted. 'Very nice girls, they good for you,
very, very cheap, no problems, you come with me, I show you,
good time, come.'

He grabbed my arm and started tugging.

'Hold on a minute, mate.' I replied, trying to release his grip on
my arm. 'Where are all these very nice girls.'

'You come, I show you girls, come this way.'

'No, I ruddy well won't unless you tell me where they are.' I
was feeling not only very impatient with this persistent so-and-so
but becoming increasingly hostile to his continued badgering.

'You heard of Cages?' he said.

'No I certainly haven't, but if that's where all your very nice
girls are, I don't think that we're the slightest bit interested, are
we?'

Richard nodded his agreement and fortunately the arrival of a
taxi we hailed rescued us from our persistent friend.

'Where to?' we were asked.

'Something Gardens,' I replied. 'It's slipped my mind.'

'I know,' said the driver. 'I'll take you, no problem.' And with
that he shut his glass partition and we sped off.

'You know, Richard, surely there must be more than one place
in Bombay ending in Gardens. Anyway, I've remembered the full
name now, it's the Hanging Gardens,' I added.

We'd arrived, and after jumping out and paying the driver, who
promptly sped away, we both instinctively felt we weren't where
we were supposed to be.

'For a start,' I said, 'We should have taken at least twenty minutes to get here instead of half that time. Where's all that smoke
coming from?' I added, referring to several columns of wispy
smoke that were drifting over the high walls surrounding goodness knows what.

63

'It doesn't look as if it's from burning garden rubbish to me.' Richard was obviously as puzzled as I was.

We walked over to the large entrance gates, where we were greeted by a sign, partly in English, which stated 'Hindu Burning and Burial Grounds. Entrance forbidden to Non Hindus.'

'Absolutely great, Sixer. What a start to our grand tour of Bombay. Mind you, I suppose when you think about it, there can't be much to choose between the Hanging Gardens and the burning ones, if you go by their names. Anyway, as we are here, I might as well try and take a few feet of film, if only to record our blunder.'

'Are you sure, Paul? I can't help but think they won't be at all pleased with you. Mind you, up to now, nobody looks all that unfriendly.' As he spoke, an official-looking gentleman, lacking uniform, made his way over to us.

'You need film, sir?' he enquired.

He had obviously attached some significance to our arrival by taxi, as apparently did the ever-increasing crowd of spectators.

Our official friend explained that for a fee of five rupees, his rules would allow us entry strictly for filming purposes only.

'In for a penny, in for a pound – or rather, a few rupees,' I said to Richard as I handed over the requested fee.

My attempts to capture on film the atmosphere, the sadness and the poignancy of the scene that unfolded before us as we walked slowly through the grounds was never going to be a resounding success, simply because it seemed half of the population of Bombay insisted on cremating their loved ones with smiling faces combined with over-indulgent waves to the camera.

'I think that's enough, Richard. Let's be on our way before we're trampled underfoot and become martyrs to our own cause.'

We waved goodbye to the enthusiastic entourage and hailed another taxi, hoping for better luck this time.

'Hanging Gardens, I know well, no trouble.' Our cabbie left us in no doubt that our journey would end up with us at the correct destination this time. We sped off again at high speed, passing right through the centre of Bombay, the streets bustling with traffic and pedestrians as usual.

'It's bloody frightening the way he's driving.' The Sixer's voice echoed his concern for his personal safety.

I wasn't listening, or looking for that matter, except through the viewfinder of my cine camera, trying to point it in the general direction we were going. If fate deemed we were to end up as road accident statistics, I was determined to record the events in the best way possible. Of one thing there could be no doubt at all, our cabbie was displaying the driving antics of a madman hotly pursued by the devil himself. Whilst we had no regrets about leaving our previous location, we had no designs on arriving at the next location with that degree of haste.

Amazingly enough, our luck held.

The Hanging Gardens are situated on high ground overlooking the sea approach to Bombay and must be one of the most pleasantly cool places in the whole area, relatively speaking. A veritable world of delight for children, their favourite nursery rhyme characters being part of a brilliantly colourful scene.

'Just look over there, Paul, by Old Mother Hubbard's shoe.'

Richard had drawn my attention to a young girl gazing up wondrously at the top window in the shoe some 20 feet above ground level.

From the window, the Old Lady herself was casting a knowing glance at the scene below, totally oblivious of the excitement she had stirred in her little admirer.

'It's certainly a city of contrasts, Richard. These gardens are as splendid as any you could find anywhere in the world. Just look at the people and the kids. Smartly dressed, lively and smashing to have around and yet, barely a stone's throw away, there's grinding poverty the likes of which I never thought I'd see. What's gone wrong?' I asked.

'I haven't really a clue. Could it be anything to do with the caste system, or probably difficulties in making their birth control policy work?' my colleague ventured.

'Come to think about it,' I replied, 'didn't the government threaten to curtail the activities of fathers of large families, so to speak. There was such a backlash from the population, they're offering worldly goods like portable radios and such as bribes to try and persuade them to toe the line, I think.'

Judging by the number of birth control clinics that advertised their presence by having massive hoardings stretching to the skyline, it looked as if the message was only slowly getting through, despite the government's threat of the chop.

We made our way back in the fading light, through darkened deserted streets, feeling not the least bit threatened by either the circumstances or the surroundings. What was becoming increasingly obvious to me was the apparent acceptance, by the less well off, of their underprivileged existence. No bitterness, no jealousy, more a recognition that life can just as easily inflict a decisive blow on the shoulders of those who have everything that money can buy. At least they would be spared that particular fate.

'Deep in thought, Paul? How about a quick trip to the Cages to see the "birds" before they fly?'

'No thanks,' I replied. 'I'd rather stick to the less flighty type.'

We were nearing the dock entrance and, once again from out of the blue, the beggar children reappeared, their wide-eyed faces eager for anything that was offered to them.

'Right, Paul, grab your loose change, then when I say so, we'll spin round suddenly, hurl the cash in their direction and then sprint for the ship's gangway.'

The die was cast. All we had to do was carry out the grand plan.

Gasping, breathless as we clambered up the gangway, only seconds in front of our new-found admirers in hot pursuit, I just hoped that we would have no need to go back ashore again before we sailed.

'That was too close for comfort,' Richard commented. 'I guess I totally underestimated their turn of speed. How can kids with their disabilities move like they do? Lack of food doesn't seem to slow them down either.'

As it turned out, we had no further chance to leave the ship. The Second Engineer decided that our wanderings had gone on for long enough and it was time to earn our living again. The 'birds' in their Cages would remain at a safe distance, at least for this trip.

What was concerning me more was how long should I leave my exposed cine film unprocessed in such high temperatures and humidity. After much thought, I decided the lesser of the evils would be to have the films developed at the Kodak processing laboratories in Bombay and trust to luck that they would catch me up at our next port and before we left the Indian coast.

As we sailed from the port and with a backwards glance at the 'Gate of India', ironically the traditional way of entering Bombay from the sea, feelings of disbelief passed through my mind. India has so much to offer, if only their politicians could get their acts together. Probably it is wrong to blame the politicians for the social muddle that seems to penetrate deep into Indian society. There again, it will be claimed that there is no muddle, just an ordered regime that tolerates social inequalities and maimed children as beggars. Whether or not they would survive was truly a matter of conjecture. The 'Gate', yes, of course, it would survive.

9

'How far to Cochin, then?' asked the Sixer.

'According to the atlas, it's about halfway down the coast from Bombay. I guess it's going to get even more humid,' I replied.

Unfortunately, the Second Engineer still showed no signs of acknowledging that we were only human beings and if he didn't ease off on the pressure down below, something drastic was going to happen. The Chief was obviously aware that a crisis was looming but he showed no sign of intervening despite the concern that the Deck Department had demonstrated for our plight. What happened next, though, was not expected by any of us.

We were about one hour into the afternoon watch when the Second said he was going up topsides to do some paperwork. I saw him climb the engine room ladders, probably a little slower than normal, understandably in the sweltering heat.

The watch continued until the meal relief time. The Sixer came rushing down the ladders, shouting that he'd found the Second Engineer just inside the engine room entrance, out for the count.

'You stay right here, Sixer, next to the phone,' I said. 'I'm going up topsides to see what's going on. The Third should be down in a minute or so.'

By the time I reached the scene, one and all were present. The Second Mate diagnosed heat exhaustion, a not surprising conclusion, given the temperature, the humidity and the extremely uncomfortable working conditions for the watchkeeping engineers.

We manhandled his apparently lifeless form onto the deck, which, given his size and weight, was no mean feat in itself. Surrounded as we were by onlookers from the Deck and Catering

Departments, one could clearly hear their comments and verdicts such as:

'Ah well, one less mouth to feed, maybe.'

'I've got just the wood to make him a launch platform' (referring to burial at sea!).

'Silly bugger, thinks he knows it all. He should remember to take his salt tablets' – and so on.

The Mate appeared on the scene and had a quick word with the Chief. 'When he comes round, he'll be in agony for sure – cramp and the like – it won't be a pretty scene.'

Indeed, the Mate was very perceptive and there was no doubt at all the Chief was going to have to intervene, if only to save the Second from himself.

There was also little doubt that the Chief had had a real fright, but even so, we were not a little surprised when he berated the Second in front of us all.

'If you carry on, Second, running yourself and the others in the department in a manner more akin to a slave ship, we'll never make it back to the UK. For heaven's sake, make allowance for the conditions and make sure you and the others take your salt tablets, otherwise I'll end up being the sole survivor of the department.'

The Second was speechless. Whether it was his condition or the effect of the Chief's dressing-down in front of the junior ranks, I couldn't guess, but for whatever reason, the look on the Second's face was a sight to behold.

'Sorry you missed all the action, Sixer, but I guess times will be a-changing, as they say.'

'Well, you know what they say, Paul – it always comes to those who wait.'

I failed to see the relevance of his logic but I didn't argue with him.

As it turned out in fact, times did change but, yet again, not quite in the manner we had imagined.

The Chief decided that the Second would come off watchkeeping for the time being, the Third Engineer would take the Second's watch, the Fourth Engineer take the Third's watch with the Sixer and, as for me, I was being temporarily promoted to take the

Fourth's watch with the Chief. All very confusing, especially for those calling the next watch.

One of the immediate improvements I was thankful for was to get a full night's rest instead of being rudely wakened at ridiculous hours.

As the saying goes, it never rains but it pours – except, of course, in India.

'We're getting extremely low on water, Fiver.' The Chief had come down below as we lay at anchor off Cochin.

'Can't we manage until we get alongside, Chief?' I enquired.

'But we're not going alongside, Fiver. We are remaining at anchor at Cochin and, as far as I can gather, also the remaining loading ports. There's little chance of us taking on water again until we return to Aden for bunkers, on the way home.'

The Chief was a far from happy man. It seemed that little or no consideration was being given to his requirements.

'What we are going to have to do is to get the desalination plant into operation, then we can make our own fresh water from sea water for the boilers. We'll leave it to the Deck Department to sort out the drinking and domestic water requirements. They'll probably be able to get supplies from water tenders.'

It didn't look to me as if the water-making plant had been in use for many a year and I couldn't help but feel sorry for the Chief having this problem to resolve on top of everything that had happened to date.

He took me on a conducted tour of the plant, explaining in great detail the method of operation, and then commenced to try and coax it into life.

'The most important thing to remember is to operate the plant as efficiently as possible. It's not a cheap way of getting fresh water and if you fall to sleep on the job, so to speak, our precious fuel bunkers will become as sparse as the fresh water we're currently left with.'

The Chief laboured hard to persuade the plant to co-operate with him, but slowly and surely, fresh water started to enter our boiler feed water tanks, of good enough quality to present no problems.

A rueful grin appeared on the Chief's face as he declared, 'It's longer than I care to remember since I last operated this equipment but I obviously haven't lost my touch. Right, we'll start topping up the boiler water levels next, and then after that, you can take over and fill the feed tanks. At least that will give us peace of mind for the time being. By the way, make sure the Fourth and Sixth Engineers have got the hang of operating the plant because you can never be certain how soon it will be before we are requiring to use it next.'

The main problem with operating the desalination plant was the extra heat it generated in the engine room and, obviously, this added to the overall discomfort of all concerned, with tempers fraying frequently.

The Deck Department didn't help by insisting that we limit our showers so as to conserve drinking water. The Chief nearly exploded because he only too well knew that about the only thing that kept us going until the end of the watch was the lovely thought of a total-immersion shower and a change into tropical whites.

No sooner had the Second Engineer recovered sufficiently enough to return to watches than the Third Engineer decided it was time to develop a fever and take to his bunk. So the poor old Fourth Engineer, having just got back on his own watch, was yet again reshuffled and put back on the Third's watch, with the Sixer and me taking the Fourth's watch.

Having departed from Cochin, we then steamed on to Calicut and then Alleppey, where we loaded further cargo. Just as the Chief had told me, the cargo was loaded from barges whilst we remained at anchor with no shore leave granted.

The food on board was becoming deplorable, there being little choice available, and with our showers diminishing at an ever-increasing rate, the need for unlimited fresh water out of our taps was becoming almost mental torture. To make matters even worse, the boatmen unbelievably went on strike at Alleppey, which meant the cargo couldn't be brought out to us. Only the cargo winches appreciated the break.

Each day was becoming interminable, our only thought was to be heading back westwards-bound across the Indian Ocean.

Loading was, at last, completed at Alleppey on Christmas Eve and, with an enormous feeling of relief, we were finally on our way, with the Third Engineer re-emerging from hibernation to take his rightful part in the proceedings.

If anyone had any allusions that Christmas Day was going to be in the slightest way joyous, they were soon to be disappointed. Various suggestions were put to the Chief Steward as to what he should do with his Christmas puddings, none of which included eating them and, in fact, if some of the suggestions had been adopted, edible considerations would definitely have gone through the window.

I was slightly more fortunate than the others because shortly before we left Alleppey, the agent boarded the vessel with a sackful of mail which included a large packet with a Kodak logo in the top left corner and my own handwritten address label slap in the middle. Much to my surprise and relief, Kodak had met the stringent processing deadline I'd given them, but only just. Despite being naturally curious to see the results of my efforts with the camera as I had no means of viewing them with me, the best I could do would be to unwind a few feet and try to sight the frames by holding the film up to the overhead light.

Because of all that was happening at that time, I'd not even got round to opening the envelope. So on Christmas Day, unbeknown to the others, I had a private preview and couldn't believe what I was seeing. From what I could discern from the 8-mm size frames, the quality was exceptional and I just hoped that there would not be a requirement to edit out too much waste as is sometimes necessary because of poor results. As my camera was fitted with semi-automatic exposure control, it was possible for me to allow for varying lighting conditions during shooting, which a fully automatic camera couldn't handle. Of course, I had to promise to give a film show on our return and just hope that it would get forgotten.

Our day passed quietly and unemotionally, and no doubt the others, like me, were hoping that if we were ever called upon to spend another Christmas away from the UK, the circumstances at that time would allow us to have a great time with an atmosphere more conducive to happiness.

Counting the days to our arrival at Aden became a top priority.

'We should be arriving at Aden day after tomorrow to take on bunkers and water.' The Chief was trying to arouse some interest in the forthcoming event but he was not having a great deal of success.

We moored at the bunkering station on arrival and in no time, the operations were under way, smoothly and efficiently in a good-humoured and polite manner, with all seeming to be well. There was no reason to suspect that any subterfuge had taken place, with the fuel samples provided by the Aden station looking quite normal and in order.

After we departed from Aden, it was the Mate who first suspected that possibly something was amiss, at least with what was emerging from our funnel. We were steaming up the Red Sea towards the Suez Canal when he telephoned below and asked why we hadn't requested the usual clearance for blowing the boiler tubes.

Having advised him that we were not doing that operation, a quick visit on deck confirmed that vast quantities of black smoke were issuing forth, creating the effect of a gigantic smokescreen.

By now the poor Chief was wondering just how much more misery was going to be inflicted on his department. We tried everything possible to reduce both the quantity and the black nature of the smoke. First we raised then lowered the temperature of the fuel before combustion, but no change occurred with the muck emanating from the funnel. Next we changed the air-to-fuel ratio through all of the possible combinations available, but again, this had not the slightest effect. Next we changed the sizes and shapes of the fuel atomisers, but despite all our efforts, our progress up the Red Sea remained clearly defined by a pall of black smoke.

The Chief still insisted that we request clearance from the bridge before blowing the boiler tubes despite the situation at the funnel-top level not changing one iota between blowing and not. As the Mate put it one day rather succinctly when I called him,

'No reasonable request to make smoke will be refused provided it's either between midnight and midday or between midday and midnight!'

It transpired that no vessels were coming within view of us, possibly for fear of emerging in a soot- and smoke-blackened condition. Our crew laboured every day on deck with hoses and mops in a battle with the elements issuing forth constantly from our funnel. This even prompted the Second Engineer to break his duck, humour-wise, when he was heard to say in response to an umpteenth request from the bridge for 'Water on deck, please,' 'There's more bloody water passing over the decks of this vessel than underneath it.' That witticism from him was the high point of his humour for the voyage.

The Chief's concern that further problems with the boilers would occur if we didn't manage to control the smoke situation fortunately didn't prove to be the case, and after steaming north through the Bay of Biscay, the English Channel was finally in sight.

After a period away from the UK, and particularly in hot and sticky places, the most alluring sight that welcomes the seafarer is the greenness of the English landscape as it comes into view on the port bow. If he wasn't getting in a bit of a state with himself in anticipation of home comforts being restored, then no doubt the beauty and relative tranquillity of the coastal scene would be sufficient to remind him how lucky we are in the UK to have such a wealth of choice with our surroundings in what is really only a mere postage stamp size area when compared with, say the USA.

Despite the time of year, with the cold really being felt, I was only too pleased to get out on deck and take the scene in. The cold seemed a small price to pay for the joy of returning to something more approaching normality.

At last the words I thought we were never going to hear reached my ears through the engine room headphones, 'Dungeness pilot on board, give us normal full speed ahead, Fiver, then remain on stand-by, please.'

'With the greatest of pleasure,' I replied.

We berthed in London on 15 January 1961 and a relief crew

appeared to bring to an end, for us, a somewhat testing and eventful voyage – or at least that is what should have happened.

The only problem was that the relief crew did not include Fifth and Sixth Engineers, so, to our chagrin, we both had to remain on board for the coasting voyage around the UK discharging ports, which included Middlesbrough and finally ended with our starting port, Birkenhead. We signed off articles there on 15 February. It did occur to me that there was just a remote chance that a certain young lady might have liked to see me again, but that would have to wait.

10

The only thing certain about shipping is the uncertainty.

Just as I was starting to relax after the hassle of the Indian voyage, I received notification from the company that I was being promoted to Fourth Engineer and was required to join the *Leo* on 21 February. Quite naturally, I had mixed feelings about this; on the one hand I was delighted to be promoted but not at all happy about having to sail again so soon after the end of what had been a truly exhausting voyage.

Nevertheless, once on board the *Leo*, it soon became obvious to me that the officers and crew of this vessel had a much better working relationship and, if the rumours were true, at least they tried to play hard as well as work hard. In fact, the Second Mate wasted little time in telling me of his plans to set up a gambling casino on board. Apparently he was motivated by the need to make a bit of money on the side to fund his shore-going leisure pursuits abroad.

Another surprise was the Chief Engineer's enthusiasm for enjoying life when the time and circumstances permitted, a philosophy also shared by the Second Engineer, whose Royal Naval background had also apparently taught him to play as hard as he worked. The Third Engineer was another remarkable character, whose girlfriend was a BOAC air hostess flying on Comet jet airliners. The Third, yet again, was a firm believer in living for the moment and had a wicked sense of humour.

At least it looked as if life would not only be bearable but possibly reasonably enjoyable, particularly as there was no regular captain for the vessel, the practice being that a master would sail for just two or three voyages on a rota basis and then be relieved.

It also transpired that beards were the in thing amongst the officers so, for the first time in my life, I ventured forth with propagating one.

Even our passengers were a jovial bunch, and having got wind of the fact that roulette, at the very least, was taking place below deck, insisted on joining in unofficially.

Watchkeeping on the 8 to 12 watch was certainly a refreshing change from the 4 to 8 watch, particularly the early morning session, although this meant that I missed the early evening sessions in our casino. Even before we had crossed the Bay of Biscay, the Second Mate was obviously on the make, so to speak, revealing a mercurial glint in his eyes, proving once again that the bank never loses. Benghazi passed almost unnoticed by the passengers, so intent were they on losing their money. They seemed quite torn between going ashore to see the sights as scheduled and trying to recoup their gaming losses.

Little did I know at that time that one of the biggest gaming casinos in North Africa was only a stone's throw from the vessel's berth. Being the duty engineer, I wasn't going to get ashore anyway, so at least my money was temporarily safe.

The weather was also proving to be exceptionally kind and our passage from Benghazi across the Mediterranean to Messina then Bari and on up the Adriatic Sea to Trieste was like sailing on the proverbial millpond.

Approaching Trieste, the view is nothing short of spectacular, with the mountains rising dramatically above the town and providing a wonderful backdrop. The Second Engineer decided that we had earned a few hours' break from a continuous day and night routine lasting nearly a fortnight.

After leaving Benghazi we had proceeded first to Messina in Sicily to take on fuel bunkers, which lasted into the early hours, then we pressed on to Bari on the south-east coast of Italy to load a refrigerated cargo. All of these passages were undertaken overnight with normal watchkeeping, followed by daywork in each port, so the opportunity to get ashore in Trieste was eagerly taken, if only to get a break from shipboard routine.

What was so noticeable about the shop window displays was the unmistakable and individual Italian design of the goods on display, particularly the clothes, shoes and glassware. They really stood out and demanded attention.

One unexpected surprise was the weather. Despite the glorious sunshine, it was extremely chilly, which we were told was caused by cold winds blowing down from the mountain tops to the sea. The locals were wearing overcoats, hats and scarves, so obviously they were used to warmer weather.

On returning to the vessel, it came as no surprise to learn that we would be sailing in the early evening in order to arrive at Venice the next morning ready to start cargo working. It was obvious that our whole schedule was geared to early morning arrivals in port, and not until we had sailed from our last loading port in the Mediterranean would we settle down to a more equable regime.

Of course, for the passengers, the schedule was ideal, giving them plenty of opportunity to take in the sights ashore during the day. Leaving the port during the early evening also gave them the chance to view the often mysteriously and curiously lit coastline, the lights sometimes so few they were barely visible and at other times so well illuminated one could be forgiven for believing that daylight had arrived early.

Next port of arrival was Venice. Despite everything one seems to have heard beforehand about this place, it really does come as a surprise to the uninitiated. It's not so much the number of canals there are but the feeling that with no streets, one would be almost certainly obliged to use either the water buses or taxis to get around. Of course, there are plenty of pedestrian walkways but even these are in the main fairly narrow and in places almost claustrophobic. Another surprise was the number of gondolas that had been laid up for the winter.

There's only one way to approach Venice to experience its true magic and that is, of course, on water but preferably whilst on the deck of a vessel rather than in the engine room. This meant that I was not going to see the waterway to beat them all, the Grand Canal. That pleasure would have to await a later visit.

So much has been written about Venice but not all of it, by any means, relates to the contrasts and ironies that abound and yet somehow remain almost camouflaged and undetected by the tourists. The true irony about the place is that without the tourists, Venice would literally sink without trace. Yet their very presence and the need to provide them with all the amenities they require is gradually destroying the environment they so eagerly admire. The buildings and the waterways are being continually eroded and undermined, with the tourist traffic contributing to some significant extent, therefore the efforts of the civil engineers and hydrographic specialists to win their battles against the natural and man-made hostile elements are to be truly applauded.

One cannot fail to register a reaction to the incredible symbolism, beauty and dimension of the buildings, exemplified by the architecture of the St Mark's Square. Yet, just below the surface, lingering doubts persist: will all this architectural symbolism survive? The self-inflicted destruction increasingly eats away at the veneer and, somehow, a cure has to be found to overcome this, otherwise a unique city will submerge once and for all.

There again, the city has survived many previous ordeals, not least one involving a certain second engineer who unfortunately climbed the tower of St Mark's Church in a slightly inebriated state, in the mistaken belief that he had pinpointed the gentleman's loo. After relieving his bladder, according to well-established legend, he then endeavoured to flush the loo by operating the bell rope. This produced a resounding but very untimely series of chimes that startled not only the natives but many an unsuspecting visitor.

Surely the most remarkable thing about Venice must be the scale of the place. It's hard to imagine the depth of imagination that went into its creation. It would almost seem that the city was dreamt up as an exhibition of great artistic and architectural endeavour, combining amazing imagination with the engineering skills and manual dexterity of truly skilled artisans. Yet, paradoxically, there had been an almost equally incredible lack of appreciation of the practical problems arising from the construction of canals and their vulnerability to the ravages of time, also man's apparent lack of concern in preventing their demise. It is a well-known fact that Italian drivers are not the most patient of individuals and that their impatience is not restricted to wheeled vehicles. They are generally as equally determined to make their water-borne journeys with as little delay as possible, hence the speeding launches, water buses and taxis all chasing far too little water space in places, creating vast tidal waves which don't help the preservation cause at all.

Having said that, the vast bulk of the *Leo* steaming up the Grand Canal right into the heart of Venice, whilst at a much more sedate pace, must still have given the preservationists regular night-mares. Maybe the sighs issuing forth from much earlier similar events provided the name for one of the most famous bridges. If one has to choose a symbol to epitomise the romance of this fine city, the bridge captures more than the imagination. It did occur to me, as the gondolas squeezed through the bridge, that the name may have come about due to the close shaves of the gondoliers trying to avoid decapitation. It was clearly apparent that their passengers were suitably impressed with the dexterity displayed by their navigators in all respects.

A little of the romance of this fine city begins to evaporate when it comes to paying for a drink anywhere in the vicinity of St Mark's Square, particularly if one is sat at a table of one of the more famous bistros. Thoughts like, they're making hay while the sun shines, spring to mind, although not at all appropriate in the circumstances. Regrettably, despite the price paid for drinking at such choice locations, there is no protection from aerial bombard-ment by the sharp sh--ting pigeons.

The lasting memory for many who have visited Venice must be the natives themselves, many of whom work in the city and travel from their homes on the mainland, their true motivation arising from the need to make a living from the tourists. At the same time, the natives put on a brave face, very conscious of their city slowly but inevitably becoming a faded symbol of past glories yet refus-ing to accept that the ravages of time, including their own self-inflicted inconsiderate acts are hastening the end. Many would say that the locals are their own worst enemies, but whether this is true or not, worldwide efforts by many organisations, together with the Italian authorities, have fought to maintain the existence and sur-vival of the city's fabric. It would be the ultimate irony if the city were to succumb to the ever-rising sea levels being experienced on a worldwide basis.

Music of many different types and styles has always been a true love of my life, and whilst I've never learnt to play an instrument properly, I have been known to produce something akin to a melodic noise whilst tinkering on the ivories. What I've always found mystifying is why people choose to play stringed instruments, particularly guitars and such. I did once try to master the intricacies of the guitar but was defeated by the down-right misery of extremely sore and blistered fingertips. Do the accomplished exponents of these instruments have nerveless fingertips?

These thoughts were certainly not passing through my mind as the beautifully melodic sounds of 'Come Back to Sorrento' drifted through my cabin porthole as we lay moored in Messina harbour. It was the faintly banjoistic sounds that intrigued as I made my way on to deck with the intention of tracing their origin.

What I discovered, as I stepped ashore, was a whole proliferation of different stringed instruments leaning against the harbour quay wall with a well-chiselled featured, deeply bronzed and aged Sicilian giving it his all.

I made the fundamental mistake of showing too much enthusiasm, whereupon our music-maker abruptly ceased strumming and handed me the instrument as if he was inviting me to drive his favourite Ferrari. If it had been such a machine then, just maybe, I would have stood a chance of performing a reasonable getaway but, as it was, I just had to try and produce something akin to a melodic sound, particularly as a crowd was beginning to gather, more in curiosity than hope. My poor fingertips protested vehemently because of having to cope with double stringing but, at last, the penny dropped.

'Very good, you like?' he smiled.

'Oh yes, just fine,' I lied. I just had to get the deal over as quickly as possible if only to hide my ever increasing embarrassment. '*Quanta costa?*' I asked. The only Italian I knew.

'For you, my friend, a gift at seventeen thousand liras, OK?'

That price didn't seem too much to pay for what, in a capable musician's hands, was undoubtedly a fine banjolin. To his undisguised delight, I accepted his offer and became the proud owner of a hand-made Sicilian musical instrument.

Unfortunately, my fellow officers demonstrated little enthusiasm for my new acquisition.

'Please don't practise anywhere near our cabins or you'll end up getting the ruddy thing wrapped round your head.' That was the Second Engineer's uncharacteristic response to the new situation.

I reckoned I'd have enough headaches learning how to play the wretched instrument without suffering any additional pain in the manner prescribed by the Second, so I reluctantly agreed. Whenever I felt the urge to perform or at least practise, I proceeded to the forecastle deck and, whilst leaning on the windlass, strummed away until my fingertips protested in the predictable way.

Had I been blessed with second sight and foreseen my ultimate fate with the instrument, then, without doubt, I would have abandoned at least the instrument and maybe even the ship.

Once again, due to the short duration of our stay, there wasn't sufficient time for a trip ashore. This was rather unfortunate as my new musical acquisition was attracting a fair amount of attention, not all of which was welcome, when I remained on board to practise.

'We're bunkering as usual at Ceuta, Fourth, and should be arriving at about twenty-three hundred hours. Let me have the fuel book after you've sounded all the tanks, then I can do my usual calculations and see how much we require.'

The Chief liked to have everything well organised and was not at all concerned that my involvement with the bunkering would last long after the end of my normal watch and into the early hours, but being the Fourth Engineer meant it was your responsibility to ensure the fuel reached all the places it was intended to, without any spillage or drama on board or ashore at the oil terminal.

I'd learnt that one way of avoiding fuel spills when bunkering the fuel oil tanks was to slightly list the vessel first one way then the other because, by doing this, a tank could be completely filled without causing an airlock. With the vessel slightly listed to port, the starboard double-bottom tanks would each be completely filled in turn with not a hint of an overflow, and similarly the opposite side tanks would be completely filled after the vessel was carefully listed slightly to starboard.

The fact that an overflow onto the decks of the vessel could happen in seconds, with dire consequences, if proper attention wasn't maintained meant that one's thoughts were totally focused on the job in hand. Particular care was necessary to allow only just sufficient fuel into the trimming tank to obtain the desired list, otherwise extreme difficulty could be experienced in persuading the vessel to list in the opposite direction in order to completely fill the opposite side tanks. It may sound quite a complicated procedure to the uninitiated but is mainly based on common sense. The trouble with bunkering in the middle of the night after two watchkeeping periods is staying awake and making split-second judgements as to when to start closing tank valves, given that the several seconds required to do this, may be just one or two too many if one started too late.

Provided that all went according to plan and the fuel entered the intended fuel tanks, the only other excitement that could occur was obtaining agreement with the bunkering station's representatives as to just how much fuel they had supplied. In order to allow for differences in the figures, the Chief usually kept a few tons up his sleeve just in case they claimed they had supplied us with more than was the case. Generally we were supplied with a little more than stated, which meant that we were able to pile on the coals, figuratively speaking, to try and make up for lost time because of bad weather or cargo delays in port when the occasion demanded.

It was always a relief to complete the bunkering operation with no drama and a little fuel in hand even if, as on this occasion, one was exhausted, hot, hungry and due back on watch in a couple of hours.

After departing from Ceuta, it was decided by the powers that be, that beard-judging time had arrived. It was hardly a contest because the Mate had an enormously unfair advantage over the rest of us. He'd been cultivating his fungal growth since leaving the cradle – or so it seemed to us. Anyway, he graciously accepted his hands-down win and promised not to shave it off. For myself, it was a welcome relief to despatch my beard to the waste bin. I'd already decided that it would not only be the first beard I'd grown but the last, certainly in hot climates. The wretched itching just wasn't worth it.

The voyage had proceeded relatively smoothly and I was looking forward to completing my first trip as Fourth Engineer. Probably the most satisfying aspect had been the team approach to running the vessel by all concerned, a more than pleasant change from my previous vessel. The only slight disappointment had been the rather advanced age of many of our passengers, although they too had accepted the ups and downs of the trip with good humour and patience.

London, even in early April, can hang heavy if one is anxious to be home, therefore as soon as our reliefs arrived on board, we were off our starting blocks like greyhounds with a fortune to win for their lucky owners.

11

Our time off between voyages passed incredibly quickly and after what seemed only a fleeting break, it was soon time to speed back to London to rejoin the ship. There had been no changes with the officers and crew but our passengers certainly seemed a much more lively bunch than the previous ones, judging by the squeals and hoots of laughter that came cascading down from the passenger deck above, the night before we sailed. They were obviously determined to enjoy themselves come what may, even hell or high water.

'I can't wait for midnight, it's been a long day.'

The donkeyman wasn't too impressed with what I'd just said as he joined me on watch at 8.00 p.m. I had been down below since 6.00 p.m. because of us anchoring in the lower reaches of the River Thames after sailing from our usual berth in the Millwall Dock. The reasons for us proceeding to this anchorage was so that we could load a part cargo of high explosives in our numbers 1 and 2 cargo holds and intended for discharge at Tripoli. We were advised that the detonators for this cargo were being stowed separately on the after deck for safety reasons. This was meant to be reassuring to us all! At last, the winches were silent. Stand by. We were ready for weighing anchor and soon were on our way, on sea pilotage, heading for the English Channel and the Dungeness pilot station in order to disembark our pilot.

'I'll see if I can get clearance from the bridge to blow the boiler tubes in a few minutes' time,' I advised the boiler room on the intercom and the donkeyman to his face. Whilst it was becoming a matter of urgency to deal with this operation, nevertheless, because we were on standby for the pilotage, it was extremely important to maintain an immediate response to any telegraph orders required by the bridge.

No sooner had I announced my intentions than the hammering jarring ringing of the telegraph brought me abruptly to my senses. I glanced quickly at the telegraph. It wasn't good news. Full astern had been ordered by the bridge despite the fact that we were proceeding at probably 14 knots. As I swung the telegraph handle to acknowledge the movement, there was a double ring full astern, followed almost simultaneously by a triple full astern.

Manoeuvring main engines full astern on any vessel proceeding at full service speed is an almost impossible task because of the turning effect on the propeller. But it was obvious that there were dire circumstances ahead.

After what seemed an eternity but was, in fact, only a few seconds, I managed to bring the engines to a standstill. Then followed a battle royal to persuade them to go not only astern but emergency full astern. I quickly decided that the only hope of achieving this would be to admit full boiler pressure steam directly into the engine cylinders through the impulse valves that were supposed to be used only for engine-starting purposes. It looked as if there was little to be lost and a lot to be gained if this worked. It did, and as I heaved a sigh of relief and with the main manoeuvring valve full open, the engine astern speed rapidly increased. The boiler room telegraph decided to choose the worst possible time to throw a wobbler so I dashed to the boiler room entrance to shout a warning to the fireman but the words didn't have time to escape my lips.

The collision was enormous. I was catapulted forward into the boiler room, then, as the vessel rolled heavily first to port with me on my backside trying not to be deposited into the bilges, we rolled right over the opposite way and I was thrown back across the plates.

'Are you OK?' I yelled at my fellow watchkeepers. They were shocked but apparently uninjured as they'd hung on for grim death whilst the vessel performed in an unimaginable manner.

The telegraph once again burst into life. 'Stop' rang out and as I answered the order and wound closed the engine stop valve, the Third Engineer appeared before me, holding my life jacket. He was limping badly and had apparently been flung out of his bunk

86

by the force of the collision impact and managed to get tangled up with his chair just for good measure. His descent to the bottom plate level in the engine room must have been extremely painful but it was good to see his reassuring face. He was followed almost immediately afterwards by the Chief and Second Engineers, both anxious to know the worst.

We had to find out as fast as possible whether we were taking in water anywhere in the engine and boiler rooms and leaving the Third Engineer at the control station; the remaining three of us had a good inspection round, including a trip down the propeller shaft tunnel.

The Chief then called the bridge. 'As far as we can see, we're OK down below. Fortunately the boiler collision chocks have done their job.'

One can hardly begin to imagine the consequences if those chocks had failed. Suffice to say that with ruptured steam pipes and scalding-hot boiler water escaping into all parts of the engine and boiler rooms, it is extremely doubtful if any of us on the 8 to 12 watch would have escaped with our lives.

But it wasn't those thoughts that were passing through my mind. What suddenly reared its ugly head was the thought of all that high explosive down our forward holds which, for one reason or another, had decided not to make its presence felt in the worst possible way. How we had escaped a massive explosion, I couldn't work out. The Chief called me up topsides as he could see that I was beginning to show the signs of delayed shock and suggested I grabbed a mug of strong black coffee to steady my nerves. I took my mug of coffee on deck and stood and stared in amazement at the sight that met my eyes. They say that seeing is believing. We had anchored and were lying about a quarter of a mile from the vessel we had collided with, a German coaster.

Our searchlights were playing over her hull and superstructure and it was plain to see that we had hit her about mid-length. Her shell structure was torn open to the extent that two double-decker buses could have passed through side by side. The damage appeared to extend down to just above the waterline. Luckily she was not loaded. That was obvious because I could see right into and across the cargo hold. It was also obvious that the crew were pumping out ballast water from her tanks as fast as possible to reduce her draft and raise the damage as high as possible above the sea level.

I bumped into the Chief Officer, who had been asleep at the time of the collision, and he also was in a state of shock. He suggested that I go forwards and see what little remained of our bows and the incredible shape of the remaining part that had survived the contact.

I followed his bidding and was once again awestruck at the sight that came into view in the darkness. What appeared to be a figurehead which protruded forwards turned out to be the shell plating we had peeled off the German coaster with our bows, just like a tin opener, as she scraped along our stem bar at right angles to our course.

I returned to the accommodation to find out more and what was intended next.

'How have the passengers taken it, Carol? Any of them injured?' I asked.

The stewardess was as cool as ever, taking everything in her stride.

'Well, those that were stood at the bar ended up, as you would imagine, on their backsides nearly drowned in their own drinks. Those that were sat down in the lounge and the smoke room ended up sliding in their chairs right across the ship, bouncing off other furniture but, remarkably, nobody has been badly hurt, just a few cuts and bruises. They're in total disbelief at what's happened, just like the rest of us really. How about yourself and the rest of the engine room staff?'

I told her briefly what had happened in the engine and boiler rooms.

'All I can say, Paul, is that several of the passengers remarked on how quickly those below seemed to have responded to the crisis. They said they heard the telegraph ringing repeatedly and noticed the engine noise changing shortly afterwards and thanked goodness that somebody seemed to know what they were doing,' she added.

It was some considerable time later that I was told that only 20 seconds had elapsed before the main engines were going slowly astern after the triple full astern had been rung. To me, it had seemed an eternity. Because the propeller had not raced or cavitated, we'd obtained the maximum benefit from our full astern manoeuvring such that our speed had been reduced by several knots. That reduction had more than probably saved our bacon, otherwise it would probably have been curtains for us all, the German coaster and crew and half of Margate. Dreamland would have had no alternative but to change its name.

It was then a question of waiting for tugs and assistance. A decision was taken that we should proceed under our own power as far as the Isle of Dogs on the River Thames but after that the tugs would take over and tow us through the locks and to the berth. The ensuing return voyage proved to be as demanding as one could imagine because of our changed shape, which made it extremely difficult to avoid close-quarter contacts, particularly once we were in the locks. Eventually and after much heartache, we berthed. One and all who had, or believed they had, reason to carry out the usual enquiries that follow such misadventures presented themselves on board.

We were sick at heart because we imagined that our team would end up being disbanded, with everyone being allocated other vessels, as it looked likely that a massive repair job would require to be undertaken to provide new bows, and this certainly wasn't going to happen overnight.

As it turned out, because of the enquiry that was being held, nobody was allowed to leave the vessel so we decided to set up shop again with our roulette wheel and try to make a bit of money on the side.

After the first week, I was permitted a weekend break and decided to visit my sister who lived in Whitstable. My sister and family decided my narrow escape from the proverbial jaws of disaster was just cause for celebration with a grand party. I didn't tell them that I'd already more than restored my spirits after succumbing to the temptation of shore entertainment after we'd returned to London. The fact that wife-swapping was almost an established routine in the south of England at that time had not escaped my attention, despite being single. In fact, being married was not a necessary requisite to engage in such activities, with one particular female I knew totally abandoning her rules.

I decided, rightly or wrongly depending on which position you adopt, to limit my close encounters at the forthcoming party, at least to start with, to the working side of the bar. By doing this, I was able to weigh up the opposition, the available talent and try and slip a few Mickey Finns into the drinks of my unsuspecting victims. If nothing else, this action would almost certainly ensure impromptu singing, acting and dancing routines, with an occasional vino collapso interrupting the proceedings.

This night was to prove no exception. Despite having the defensive barrier of the bar to protect me from advancing amorous females, I had sadly misjudged the mixture of the drinks, such that an unexpected trio demanded my presence in their midst to perform a singing solo. Anyone who has heard my voice would run a mile rather than make such a demand, but they were not to be defeated. I was dragged, not exactly raging or screaming, from behind the bar in order to perform.

If only I had partaken of a few more drinks, I might have been in a better position to exercise my vocal chords in a melodic manner. As it was, my performance lacked depth and penetration. The penny then dropped. The tables had been turned on me. The only forfeit they required . . . my trousers.

Only three weeks after the collision, the repairs were completed and we were ready for sailing again, our good vessel looking resplendent with a new bow and repainted overall. The big surprise was that all the original passengers returned for a second helping, no doubt convinced that lightning doesn't usually strike twice in the same place.

The sense of relief as we headed down the English Channel and passed the collision location intact, was noticeable amongst all on board, not least of all the engine room staff. Whether the Chief was trying to take his mind off the subject of collisions and high explosives was difficult to say, but before we sailed he brought his scooter on board with the intention of giving it a complete overhaul. Unfortunately his interest in this project started to wane so he got me involved, much against my better judgement. There was no doubt at all in the Chief's mind that his time would be much more profitability spent in our casino.

Our passengers, however, were definitely more interested in parties than gambling, so the Second Mate decided to invite one and all to a party after we berthed in Tunis. The invited guests included our Captain, whose party speciality involved reeling off a parable concerning a certain archbishop. He then challenged those present to follow suit, from memory and without repeating a single word. The Captain not only believed in testing one's memory cells, he also required the participants to quaff a pint of beer simultaneously. Naturally the Captain displayed remarkable dexterity and accomplished his act to loud applause, finishing his pint without spilling a drop or choking.

The 'penalty' for inadvertently repeating any part of the parable incurred a restart not only from the beginning of the piece but with a fresh pint of beer. The challenge for the females present was only slightly less daunting as they were still required to accomplish the feat with a half-pint. It soon became apparent that practice does not make perfect, as the saying goes, particularly when the lubrication for the vocal chords is alcoholic. In fact a disaster was pending, the stock of beer in the Second Mate's wardrobe was receding at an uncomfortable speed and there was real concern as to whether the party was doomed to an early demise.

Because I had an early turn-to in the morning, I decided to beat an inconspicuous retreat before I lost the battle to remain sober and ended up on the carpet, one way or another. The Second Mate's party was judged to be the highlight of the trip. I only wished I'd stayed but there was certainly a lot more to come on that trip.

Despite my intention to get ashore at Benghazi, if only to see the remarkable gambling casino I'd heard so much about, my luck was not in because of a duty night on board.

After sailing from Benghazi, we proceeded across the Mediterranean Sea towards Italy and, at last, Bari. I'd been told that the Old Town was where all the atmosphere and activity was centred, and here we were, steaming into the harbour, which was enormous, surely not in proportion to the Old Town. It was certainly

91

almost large enough to accommodate virtually the entire Italian naval fleet.

Once again, the usual routine of engine room maintenance frustrated the chances of conducting a daylight foray, but come nightfall, and beckoned by a call from on high – the Second Engineer – at last I had the chance to see for myself whether or not the fact matched the fiction. Well, that was the intention; probably I should have known better when the Chief Engineer offered to do a night on board for the Third Engineer. Our Ted enjoyed life on various levels, but not before he was steaming on all cylinders, adequately primed with copious quantities of vino plonk. The only plonk that qualified in Ted's eyes was that which the locals drank.

There we were then, the three troubadors, ready, willing and able, according to Ted. I wasn't sure at all, but he was insistent that we couldn't appreciate the delights and romance of the Old Town unless we were truly in the mood.

'Ted, listen to me. I've really had quite enough, in fact I'm more than adequately lubricated, thank you very much.'

My remarks prompted the Second Engineer to remind me of the dire consequences if I failed to turn-to the following day.

'Right,' said Ted. 'Enough's enough, food next. I know just the right place, the fish market, marvellous seafood, can't be beaten. Then we'll have a look at the Old Town and the walls.'

I had to admit the seafood was delicious, but there again, in my state, I was not in the best position to judge. There was a fair chance that almost anything served up to me would have tasted much the same and not bad at all.

We appeared to have covered a lot of ground and had taken in several more entertaining watering holes when at around 1.00 a.m. and with not many people around, Ted had one of his famous inspirational ideas.

'See up there?' said Ted.

'Yes,' said the Second and I in unison.

'It's only a bloody advertisement for a car tyre,' added the Second.

'For your information, that's a Michelin tyre advertisement,' enthused Ted.

'So bloody what? A tyre's a tyre, for heaven's sake. What's so special about a Michelin?' The Second was as puzzled as I was about Ted's sudden interest in an apparent overweight, ugly-looking individual shaped like an over inflated windbag.

'Look, you two, just keep a lookout,' he requested.

Before we could intervene, Ted was shinning up the column that was supporting the advertisement; this was all of 20 feet high.

What followed in the next 15 minutes or so will forever remain etched in my memory. Ear-piercing whistles, shouting from all directions, shots being fired, hopefully in the air, then my feet running faster than I'd ever thought possible, the Second shouting, 'This way, quick, before they spot us.'

My God, I thought, I've only been at sea five minutes and I'm going to be shot.

'We'll have to jump.' The Second was insistent.

'Look at that bloody drop. We'll kill ourselves.' I pleaded.

But one glance at the Second's face was enough to make up my mind. Better dead by jumping than by shooting.

By some miracle, we landed on our backsides on soft mud at the foot of the wall.

'OK?'

'Yes Second. What now?'

'That's the harbour road but there's no point in trying to enter at the main gate, they'll have been warned. There's another entrance where there's some building work going on. We'll have to try that and hope for the best.'

Running like bats out of hell, we entered the netting enclosure erected for the building works just as a police car rounded the bend on the harbour road at high speed.

We split up. This time luck was on my side. There, miraculously, was the ship, the gangway and safety. There was not a soul in sight as I dived into my cabin, breathless, and locked the door.

What next? I thought. What's happened to the other two?

Half an hour later, the Second appeared on board, minus his shoes, with wet concrete up to his sock tops. His short cut in the dark had come to an abrupt halt in the middle of a newly concreted base for a dock shed.

As for Ted, his story was barely credible. He reckoned that a gorgeous bit of local talent had come to his rescue, taken him in and then kept him comforted for the night. He'd certainly not been locked up and, knowing Ted, his story was more than likely perfectly true.

I was looking forward to taking some cine film in Venice as there had been no opportunity previously to get my camera rolling. We had sailed direct from Bari to Venice and were ahead of our schedule, with an overnight stay likely, but the Second Engineer was not pressing for any maintenance work to be carried out. Following our morning arrival and after a quick breakfast, Sparks and I were shorebound.

It was becoming very obvious that it would not be a straightforward case of pointing the camera in the desired direction and firing away. The main problem was achieving a good shot sequence that would not require extensive editing afterwards. This situation was arising because of the hordes of visitors conflicting with one another in the narrow walkways that seemed even narrower than they actually were because of the tunnel effect caused by the close proximity of the buildings.

It was a welcome relief to be able to film freely in St Mark's Square with only the mischievous pigeons liable to distract one's aim. I've generally tried over the years to identify the idiosyncrasies of the buildings and the natives, but as I soon found out, Venetians are, in the main, not too happy about appearing out of the blue on film, with the gondoliers no exception to this rule. This idiosyncrasy worked very much in my favour as one poor devil, in his quest to blast me verbally to the skies for having the audacity to try and record his performance, forgot to lower his head as his gondola passed below the Bridge of Sighs. How he recovered his balance and somehow managed to remain on board we couldn't begin to work out, but his choice of words appeared to be equally as dramatic as his balancing act.

After that unfortunate episode, I decided to concentrate more on inanimate objects that couldn't react in such a lively manner.

We boarded a water bus at the Grand Canal terminal and proceeded from there to the Rialto Bridge stop. The amount of traffic was unbelievable but despite this, our progress was quite rapid, with our driver demonstrating, once again, that Italians only drive at two speeds, flat out or stopped, whether it be on the roads or on water. Their natural flair for speed seems to ensure their survival, one way or another, although judging by the evidence of numerous contacts showing on the buildings and water frontages, possibly their survival relatively unscathed from these incidents, is more attributable to good fortune than to driving skill. We weren't in a position to really judge but, having said that, there were no sightings of sinking vessels or drowning people.

Sparks suggested that we should look for a bit of real action to film but, as I tried to explain to him, the chances of being in the right place at the right time to record such a sequence was about as remote as such an event actually occurring.

No sooner had I completed expounding my theory than an explosion of extremely strident vocabulary made us both spin round, with a row having broken out between a loud-mouthed young tourist yuppie and an irate shopkeeper outside his shop. It seemed neither appropriate nor prudent to try and film this little gem, for fear of becoming inadvertently involved, but I couldn't help but ponder on the loss of what would definitely have been a piece of unique film.

Getting back to the ship in time for our evening meal suddenly became a top priority as time sped on; we were not prepared to pay the going rate because, as far as we could work out, the cost of eating in cafés in Venice was prohibitive.

Despite having missed a real bit of Italian-style action, I felt that the film I had shot would hopefully capture some of the atmosphere of Venice. Time would tell.

'Well?' asked the Second Engineer on our return. 'Was it all worth the effort?'

'Hopefully, Second. I've got a good mixture of shots, but you always wish you'd filmed something more.' I didn't mention the action I had not filmed.

As usual, the passengers were full of good cheer after their Venice adventure, simply because for most of them this port was the highlight of their holiday. What surprised most of them was the port and dock area, which, whilst not all that different to more usual ports, must have come as a bit of an unexpected development if they thought of Venice purely as a symbol of the great achievements of the past.

After sailing from Venice, we were bound for Syracuse, Messina, Palermo and finally Algiers before proceeding on passage to London. The mixture of races, religions, beliefs and ways of life of the countries bounding the Mediterranean Ocean never cease to amaze me yet despite the relatively short distances separating these countries and the not too difficult approaches from the sea, there has not been a history of continual wars and invasions apart from one or two notable exceptions both from ancient and modern history. Could it be that these peoples do not wish to dominate their neighbours for political reasons or has history taught them that the price to be paid for such domination is far too high? Maybe there is too much cynicism about their politicians and their motivations to encourage them to believe what they say. Or could it be that the climate and heat just doesn't make the warring worthwhile. After all, there's more to be gained from sharing a bottle of wine with your neighbour than crashing it down on his head.

As we lay moored in the harbour at Algiers and with a hot and humid blanket of air descending on the vessel, I was suddenly reminded that my obligation as duty engineer that evening was not confined to engine room matters. A frenzied knocking on my cabin door announced the arrival of the stewardess in a panic.

'Paul, you're not going to believe this. The bar refrigerator has packed up and we're fast running out of cold drinks. Just to make matters worse, we've hardly any ice either,' she added.

I felt like saying, 'What's in it for me, if I can fix it?' but her concern ruled that out.

'I'm not an expert on bar refrigeration, Carol, but I'll have a go. If I succeed in getting it going again, I'm still going to have to wait for the only reward I'd want – a cold beer.'

I sweated for over two hours, first of all diagnosing the fault, then searching the electrical stores and many cardboard boxes until eventually a spare thermostat revealed itself. At a time approaching midnight, I was at last able to announce that the machine was operating again, by which time most of the suffering souls had given up hope and retired to their bunks.

I must admit though, the delivery of a full case of beer to my cabin next day with the compliments of the Chief Steward did make me feel my efforts had been amply rewarded. My only concern was whether or not the equipment would keep going, at least until the end of the voyage, because I doubted that I would have an answer if it failed a second time.

The air temperature did not even start to drop a little until we headed out from the Mediterranean, so on the next voyage, it was certainly likely to be extremely hot and decidedly uncomfortable for the engine room staff.

Our on-board casino was proving to be as popular as ever with the passengers, and the Second Mate could hardly conceal his joy at the undoubted windfall that had come his way as the unofficial banker. Unfortunately we were not able to plunder any of his takings after our arrival in London because our reliefs were on the quay as the ship berthed in the Millwall Dock. Our thoughts were much more concentrated on getting homeward bound rather than letting the Second Mate treat us to a night out on the town.

12

Once again, the time at home vanished almost without trace, with barely the opportunity to re-establish contacts with family and friends before heading back on the train to London.

Before my seagoing career commenced, I'd developed a passion for car rallying and, after reluctantly parting with my Sunbeam Talbot Sports Coupé because of its insatiable thirst for water which couldn't be cured, I'd purchased a new Ford Anglia. Much to the chagrin of my parents, I promptly set about tweaking up its performance, mainly utilising the especially prepared equipment which was just beginning to appear on the auto shop shelves. One disadvantage of doing this was the difficulty in hearing the verbal instructions from one's navigator. Straight-through exhaust systems show no respect for noise abatement, therefore in order not to ruin the larynx of my navigator, I came up with the idea of a two-way voice communication system based on hearing-aid equipment. Apart from having to put up with plenty of sarcastic comments from other club members, no problems arose and we reckoned we had pioneered a system, which was only to appear on the professional rally scene several years later.

Unfortunately, sailing on ships and car rallying are not at all compatible, especially when one has to give firm commitments and promises to appear on starting lines on specific dates. I was therefore faced with reluctantly having to give up the sport, and in order that my parents could use the car while I was away at sea, I reconverted it back to its normal road specification, just completing the work before I left for London.

On arriving on board the *Leo*, I discovered that we had a new Chief Engineer, who was, to say the least, immense. His size was fortunately matched by his sense of humour and patience, both of which were certainly going to be tested to their limits by forthcoming events.

Probably the first indication of things to come emanated from the Catering Department, who seemed to be totally immune to our protestations about the frequency of pork on the menu. With temperatures beginning to soar to three figures, they failed to recognise that neither the passengers nor the crew appreciated such delicacies in these conditions.

Our first stop after leaving London had, as usual, been Ceuta, to take on fuel bunkers prior to continuing on to Benghazi to discharge cargo. Whilst at Benghazi, I was asked by one of the passengers what the temperature was in the engine room. It transpired that the gentleman was the Conservative MP for Southport, and on being told that the temperature was 126°F, he expressed total disbelief. He requested permission to take a few temperatures for himself at different times and after gathering the information and discovering that the boiler room temperature was even higher on occasions, he expressed a firm commitment to try and get our working conditions improved. Of course, we all expressed our grateful acknowledgment of his concern for our well being but were not naïve enough to believe that his intervention would herald any changes whatsoever.

Our voyage itinerary again included Bari as well as Trieste and Venice, followed by Rijeka in Yugoslavia, then on to Sicily and the Lipari Islands, before proceeding up the west coast of Italy.

In view of the events that had occurred at Bari on the last voyage, none of us fancied a trip ashore for fear of being recognised. It was only after we had berthed at Trieste that I thought of spreading my wings and taking off for a decent meal. We'd learnt from passengers previously of an establishment not too far distant from the city centre that was as near as one could get to a British café in Italy. Their speciality was a variety of toasted delicacies which put beans on toast to shame. When it became known what my intentions were, I was hastily joined by other starving folks and we descended en masse to this establishment. Needless to say, the proprietors were over the moon and welcomed us with open arms, providing us with food and service that left nothing to be desired and even threw a bottle of their best house wine in free for good measure.

After wining and dining, I decided to explore the local shops. One thing I'd noticed previously was the quality and originality of many of the goods on sale. Whilst it was not a very original choice, I decided to treat myself to a quality set of drawing instruments unlike anything I'd seen in the UK. The very fact that those instruments are still in use 38 years later speaks for itself.

Because we were able to depart from Trieste earlier than normal, our passengers were in for a bit of a treat with an evening passage to Venice. The myriad of night lights of the anchored fishing vessels created what seemed like a guided route to the uninitiated, but for our navigators nothing could be further from the truth. They were, at times, stretched to their limits trying to avoid every imaginable floating object, including not a few pleasure vessels, some of which were stationary and anchored, many not. The high-speed flights of the water bus expresses crossing the extremities of the Adriatic Sea were testimony to the skill required to keep out of trouble. The sheer joy of being able to sit and relax on deck in the balmy evening temperature with an ice-cold drink to hand and witness the unfolding panorama of extremely busy shipping lanes, combined with the excitement of what must seem to be a plethora of close misses, had to be worth every penny they had paid, even allowing for the less than acceptable food they'd been dished up.

The Second Engineer decided that there was urgent maintenance work to be carried out after we arrived at Venice so no shore trips were forthcoming and, in no time at all, we were on our way to Rijeka. I'd been more than adequately briefed about the risks of stepping out of line in a Communist country, and as one walked through the city streets, a feeling of oppression literally made itself more than abundantly apparent. One could not shake off the feeling that pairs of eyes were following your very footsteps, and even looking in the shop windows, made one feel guilty of snooping. I suppose it was the look of despair on the faces of so many of the people, and particularly the children, that summed up the situation so vividly for me. Then if one wanted more proof of the hopelessness of their state, the evidence was staring me in the face as I focused my eyes further on what I originally thought was a magnificent display of clocks and watches. It slowly dawned on me that what I was really looking at was a very cleverly contrived advertisement display of cardboard mock-ups. There was little point in holding the real items in stock when the purchase prices were way beyond anything that could be afforded and, in any event, it was more than likely the goods were not available.

Whilst ashore once again that evening and having a drink in a local bar with our ship's agency representative, we had a visit from the local state police, who had not just appeared out of the blue. The agency representative was escorted outside, and whilst our immediate reaction was to go to his help, the Second Engineer advised us not to intervene unless we fancied a trip to the Siberian salt mines. We heeded his words and decided not to hang about but get back to the ship before the police decided they wanted us to accompany them also.

Our departure from Rijeka was uneventful, with the agency representative having apparently been cleared of any misdemeanour, but when we arrived in Messina, it transpired that there had been a touch of 'political trouble' there; the Mafia had been frustrated, with one of their 'deals' necessitating a reduction by one of those who were causing the frustrations.

Once again, we received informal advice about not transgressing the local laws, customs and pastimes whilst ashore, but this advice didn't extend to events of the like that had just taken place.

We were soon to learn that, despite the apparent openess of the establishments, cafés and bars in both Messina and Palermo, there were no-go areas for unsuspecting foreigners.

But standing on the deck of the vessel moored in the vastness of Palermo harbour on a glorious August morning and gazing in incredulity at the speed of the hydrofoil arriving from Reggio Calabria, literally dropping into the water only yards from the berth and losing a speed of 40 knots in as many feet, reminded me of the saying about beauty being in the eyes of the beholder. The scene that had just unfolded before me was both beautiful and breathtaking.

Our stay in Palermo was only of a few hours' duration, then it was on to Canneto in the Lipari Islands just north of Sicily, with a steaming time of just a few hours.

The sea was as perfectly blue in colour as could possibly be imagined, the sunlight cascading downwards with a brilliance and clarity almost defying description. Islands located in a dreamlike, almost mystical setting and yet, here we were, proceeding to an anchorage not just to disembark our passengers onto a shore-bound launch but to load part of the island as cargo. It is difficult to imagine that the most important activity on the Lipari Islands is the mining of pumice, of which the islands are partly made. Unless steps are taken to cut back on this mining, it is almost inevitable that the islands will shrink and eventually disappear.

The incredible clarity of the water around the vessel reminded me, once again, of the saying that seeing is believing. The depth of water at the anchorage was all of 100 feet yet the sand bed of the harbour could clearly be seen and appeared to be at hardly any depth at all.

The passengers were duly disembarked onto the pilot launch and the engineers returned down below to deal with a few pressing problems and maintain the usual watching brief on the cargo winches. As there was no other method of loading the cargo, any breakdown of the winches would have seriously disrupted the operations and delayed the vessel.

Fortunately no difficulties were experienced and immediately after we had completed loading, and with the passengers and our pilot on board, we set sail for Palermo, apparently returning to load late cargo. Our return stay at Palermo hardly seemed to justify the extra steaming time we had undertaken, particularly as our next port was to be Salerno on the west coast of Italy.

One sure way of guaranteeing plenty of action, certainly on the engine controls, is to have an Italian pilot on board. Not for the first time, handling the main engines had fallen on my shoulders. It is only when the telegraph barely stops ringing with manoeuvring orders as frequent as the drops of rain in a heavy shower that one begins to wonder what the hell is going on on the bridge. Our

102

pilot was typically impatient to complete his duties, yet his judgement was as astonishing as ever.

When I finally surfaced on deck, I just could not believe how we had managed to squeeze in and manoeuvre to our berth without a single contact with the other berthed vessels or the fixed parts of the harbour. If this particular pilot's intentions were to impress, he'd won a few admirers. Obviously when a pilot is repeatedly handling vessels in and out of the same harbour, his special knowledge of the current eddies and flows counts equally as much as his judgement of speed and directional response of the particular vessel he is piloting. Nevertheless, credit is deserved when due, and on this occasion it was the talking point on arrival, After all, we were the largest vessel that could squeeze through the harbour entrance.

Salerno is perched on the edge of the Apennine mountain range, which extends down the west coast of Italy and is undoubtedly a mixture of starkness, grandeur and beauty, with the harbour scene adding to the overall effect.

The Autostrada de Sol passes by the town and leads in the general direction of Pompeii, where time stood still when an eruption of immense proportions struck down the inhabitants centuries ago. It transpired that the local agent had organised a trip for our passengers to Pompeii, which the Captain and Chief Engineer managed to get themselves involved with. On their return, they seemed more relieved about getting back in one piece than being over the moon with their sightseeing. When the Chief explained that their driver appeared to have been putting in practice for the Italian Grand Prix, with the sheer drops either side of the autostrada obviously having no effect on him, their concern seemed well justified.

It looked as if we might proceed to Naples, passing the Isle of Capri, but this turned out not to be the case because of the number of ships already at anchor awaiting entry to this port. Therefore it was back to Messina for bunkers prior to commencing the relatively long return haul to the UK.

Once we were on our way, life settled down to the usual seagoing routine, which, after the hectic port visits, seemed a very welcome change and the 12 days passed relatively peacefully up to our arrival in London.

13

Little could I have known when we sailed on the next voyage for the Mediterranean that a chance meeting in Gibraltar with complete strangers might lead to new horizons. Just when life appears to be moving forward on a steady course, unexpected events can intervene which, if pursued, can result in dramatic turning points. The problem is that most folks don't have the vision to see the opportunities when they arise, and I'm no different to others in this respect.

Drama on our outward passage first reared its head in Benghazi when fire broke out in the number 3 hold. Fortunately it was soon extinguished before a disaster occurred, but this incident reminded us how vulnerable we were to those who did not observe the 'no smoking' rule. It looked as if I was going to remain with the vessel for some time, therefore it seemed a good idea to make some contribution to the fixtures of the vessel. It was suggested to me by the Chief Steward that a couple of ashtrays wouldn't go amiss for the passenger public areas, then the mates put in a request for one for the bridge, so I set to in the workshop with tools and some brass plate to produce the goods to their requirements. It all helped to relieve the pressures of watchkeeping, with the length of the watch seeming less than normal. The main problem was not getting carried away with the work in hand and delaying the watch duties, which would then require a last-minute superhuman effort to finish in time for the handover to the next watch.

Our itinerary was, more or less, the same as on previous voyages, except that this time our stays in both Trieste and Venice were of extremely short duration and coincided with heavy rainfall, much to the chagrin of the passengers.

The saving grace on this voyage turned out to be our new cook. His sheer ability in the food department rendered him truly a *chef de cuisine*, with dishes that would have done any top restaurant proud. It was just as well he had both the skill, also the flair and imagination to create what he did, otherwise, with relatively short stays in Bari, Canneto, Messina, Catania and Palermo, we might well have had a mutiny from the passengers. As it was, their main objective in life appeared to be confined to gorging themselves on exquisitely prepared dishes washed down by thirst-quenching drinks in one form or another. By the time we were approaching Gibraltar, their happiness was almost complete, with the earlier disappointments of Trieste and Venice long since forgotten.

I had only intended to go ashore to post some mail and stretch my legs on the evening of our arrival in Gibraltar. Walking along Main Street towards the post office, I was stopped by two English-speaking gentlemen.

'Excuse us, young man, could you point us in the direction of the post office?' They'd not been slow to notice the mail I was carrying.

'That's just where I'm heading, so I'll lead the way, if you like,' I replied.

As we walked towards the post office, it soon became obvious that the two gentlemen accompanying me were not the routine tourist types.

The one who had spoken first introduced himself as the Shell European Exploration Manager, and his colleague turned out to be an explosives expert with the nickname of Meggers.

After posting our respective mail, they asked me if I would like to join them for a drink. They were obviously genuine and, after accepting their invitation, we found our way to a local nightclub which I'd been told was well worth a visit.

The fact that we'd hardly been in the establishment for more than a few minutes when three extremely attractive young females pounced on us certainly seemed a move in the right direction. Naturally we were very much aware that it was not our charm and good looks that had attracted these young ladies to our table, more a case of mercenary pressures being exerted by their employers. Unfortunately, despite paying for genuine drinks for these bar girls, as they are termed, they're usually served nothing more alcoholic than coloured water, which does wonders for the bar profits but nothing to boost one's relationships, platonic or otherwise.

Our female friends soon decided that their employer's profits were not going to rocket because, despite the fact that they were making their own drinks disappear in a flash, we were simply not showing any inclination to follow suit.

After their departure, explained by the joint need to visit the ladies room, we relaxed, with the atmosphere of the establishment having a marginally more intoxicating effect than the drinks being served up. A few more rounds appeared on the table and we chatted about all and sundry. These guys were certainly not on a holiday on the Rock. Their mission was to search for oil and try and determine whether there was any worth recovering, which seemed to me to be a ludicrous idea, given the size of Gibraltar. What I was not aware of at that time was the political dynamite that such a discovery would have created. Any such find could have extended well beyond the confines of Gibraltar, not unlike the subsequent discoveries in the North Sea.

Further discussion revealed that Meggers had acquired his explosives acumen whilst serving with the Royal Engineers and had reached the rank of major before retiring to the relatively sedentary ranks of civvy life in the film industry. His credits at that time included *The Guns of Navarone* for work on the explosive sequences but his interests obviously extended well outside filming.

As the evening wore on and our conversations continued, I was beginning to have some difficulty controlling my mouth muscles, yet here I was talking about a subject close to my heart, and before I knew where I was, I was expounding on my own exploits in the cine field, including the inevitable wedding films but, more interestingly for them, the semi-professional motor racing filming I'd been involved with at various circuits in the UK.

Meggers decided that I possibly had the experience and motivation to develop my capabilities professionally and recommended that on the vessel's return to London, I seek an interview with the Soho Square based representative of the Cinematic, Graphic and

Technicians Union in order to get established before making over-tures to the TV networks. He then asked me if I had anything to write on, and all I could find in my pocket was an old Berenici Night Club entrance ticket from Benghazi, on which he wrote my London contact's name and address. I was advised to contact the representative immediately on our return to London and he would advise the representative accordingly.

It looked as if, provided I followed the recommended pro-cedures, I could wave goodbye to my seagoing career with the promise of much better things and rewards to follow, if I produced the required results. During the course of the next day when I was recalling the previous evening's events, I had no doubt about the genuineness of my contacts but I pondered about the qualities that were necessary to work day in and day out as a cameraman, some-times in horrendous circumstances.

I eventually decided that if I didn't give it a run, I'd always be left pondering whether or not I would have made the grade.

On the passage back to the UK I thought about the explanations that would have to be given to my current employers, my family and friends, who all, no doubt, would suggest I'd gone completely off my rocker.

As we neared the UK we received the itinerary of our discharg-ing ports and, surprise, surprise, for the very first time, London was not included. We were to discharge solely at northern ports, load at eastern ports and then proceed straight back to the Mediterranean with no reliefs available.

There was no way that I would be able to show my face in that famous office in Soho Square where so many dreams have been realised or shattered.

Shortly after sailing on our next voyage to the Mediterranean, we were quite surprised to find that heading our passenger list were no lesser persons than the recently retired Governor General of the Bahamas and his wife. As so often is the case, our honoured guests did not expect any special attention and, in fact, particularly requested that they be treated no differently to any of the other passengers. They turned out to be a very charming, witty and highly entertaining couple who also appreciated our little gaming casino. Once again, the Second Mate was on to a winner and, by our reckoning, was quickly becoming the highest paid person on board.

Following our usual bunkering stop at Ceuta, our first real port of call was again Benghazi. When the Second Engineer invited me to join him on a shore trip, I leapt at the chance. The Second's claim to fame was his unerring ability to head off in exactly the right direction so as to arrive at just the right establishment to suit his taste. This time his first port of call was the Lux Hotel and it was soon apparent that he'd hit the jackpot once again. Not only were the surroundings and service absolutely first rate, so was the company. Amongst the many and varied folks present was a crowd of locally based British service personnel who insisted we join them and return to their NAAFI for a party. Neither of us remembered much of the evening's entertainment, particularly after our arrival at the NAAFI. The generosity of our hosts resulted in us overimbibing, but fortunately also extended to making sure we arrived safely back on board despite being a little the worse for wear.

Once again, our voyage itinerary unfortunately turned out to be a big disappointment for our passengers, with no requirement for cargo discharging or loading at Trieste, Venice, Bari or any of the eastern Adriatic ports, which meant that after leaving Benghazi, we would be heading for Sicily before returning to the UK. Then out of the blue, whilst lying at our berth in Messina, we were advised that we would be loading a cargo of pumice again at the Lipari Islands, which lifted their spirits. One thing for certain, they had no inkling of the surprise that they were going to miss out on after we had arrived and were lying at anchor.

After our arrival at Messina, the Chief called me up to his cabin to advise me of the intention to try out a sample bunkering operation with the intention of determining the feasibility of taking bunkers there, instead of Ceuta, in the future because of some political problems. I didn't appreciate the timing of the exercise, which had to be fitted into the previously arranged bunkering schedule, and this meant the bunkering was to take place overnight, with me losing my night's sleep.

As it turned out, the exercise was very smooth and successful and, in many ways, was much easier to handle than in Ceuta, where a long road trip was necessary to reach the storage tanks, which the Fourth Engineer was required to sound after climbing to the top of them. The very fact that you were so far from the vessel and very much on your own didn't encourage the Fourth Engineers to get too argumentative with the oil company's representatives about the differences that frequently arose with the soundings. It always seemed that before bunkering started, the measuring tape used for sounding the shore tanks, was about 12 inches short, but after finishing the tape had grown about 24 inches. One glance at the representative's face was enough to ensure a reluctant agreement about the figures, if only to ensure a safe return to the vessel.

Once we had completed the bunkering at Messina, and as there was no possibility of us being able to commence loading cargo at the Lipari Islands until the following day, it was decided that we should remain at Messina for the morning, so allowing a shore trip for those willing and able.

On most vessels, the engineers' accommodation is in the same alleyway or at least on the same side, if not on the same deck. But on this vessel, the Fourth Engineer's cabin was on the opposite side and next to the Radio Officer's cabin. This gentleman not only worked relatively normal hours but also had a passion for the game of chess. There was no doubt about his capabilities, he could wipe the floor with most of the opposition, but as chess was definitely not my favourite game, I had no intention of getting involved.

His enthusiasm for chess was almost matched by two other loves in his life, one a lady who was far from single and, by an almost unbelievable coincidence, known by my parents as an apparently clean-living woman; the other passion was fishing in any shape or form.

Just forgetting the Radio Officer for a minute, one of the more exhilarating and refreshing experiences for a seagoing engineer is stepping out of a hot and humid engine room and escaping out onto deck on a hot summer's day with the ship at a superb anchorage, a cool can of beer in hand and a lovely view to boot.

Certainly the Lipari Islands qualified in all respects and with the vessel quietly riding the gentle swell, I was partaking of my end of watch refresher, quite carried away by the scenic vista that unfolded itself in a vast panorama and almost oblivious to other events taking place quite close at hand. I certainly hadn't noticed our Radio Officer, who was standing near the stern, rod in hand. Then a shout attracted my attention in his direction. He was struggling doggedly with something on his hook that was certainly no tiddler. As his rod flexed and bent and his reel spun like a Catherine wheel on bonfire night, word sped round the vessel, with the crew and the remaining passengers on board, appearing like magic to witness the unequal struggle between man and ...?

Despite the crystal clarity of the sea and the breathtaking underwater vista of pure white sand, coral and exotic fish only a few feet away, the water around the stern where our Radio Officer was performing was foaming and churning with almost zero visibility.

A shriek from a passenger immediately focused our attention directly on the performance on the after deck, with the Radio Officer's arm movements reminiscent of the conductor of the Boston Philharmonic Orchestra in full flow ... until he dropped his baton, or rather his rod, and ran for his life. His adversary had obviously got fed up of being tugged and heaved and literally decided to fly onto deck to take a closer look at the opposition.

I, like others witnessing this spectacle, had probably never seen anything quite like the sight that met our eyes. I thought about the expression 'the wonders of the deep'. Here, on the deck of our very own vessel, was just about the weirdest-looking amphibious creature imaginable. It turned out to be a deep-water flying fish that somehow had swum close inshore and then got tempted by the bait on the hook. After deciding that there was little of interest to detain it any longer, our amphibious friend took off again, this time for the deep but complete with rod and line, leaving our angler pondering on the hazards of sea angling and the less hazardous possibilities of fly-fishing.

It was not at all surprising that the passengers returning to the ship on the shore launch stepped with great care onto the gangway. Visions of sharing sea space even for only a few moments with such weird-looking creatures was obviously very much on their minds.

110

After the excitement of the Radio Officer's star performance, our voyage back to the UK almost paled into insignificance, although it provided us with many a talking point during the off-duty periods. The usual routine of watches, off-watch relaxation with a bit of gaming thrown in for good measure, helped to pass the time until we reached our London berth. I often reflected on the good times I'd had whilst crossing the Western Ocean, but on these voyages our passengers, whilst frequently being great to get on with socially, lacked the youth, vitality and vivaciousness of those on the earlier voyages.

14

As it looked likely that I would continue sailing from London for the foreseeable future, I had decided to bring my car to town to have it available for use, particularly in view of the increasing difficulty in getting relieved on arrival back. So after berthing in London and on my first free half-day, I took it on myself to try and locate an old girlfriend who I knew was teaching in a north London school. Her whereabouts were unknown to me apart from the name of her school and, in desperation, I tried the nearest local library to see if she was a member.

Looking back now, such an enquiry, whilst audacious, would not then have been considered outrageous; unfortunately nowadays the same enquiry, unless from a police officer, would probably result in a quick appearance from the boys in blue themselves.

The librarian was at first naturally reluctant to reveal any information but after I'd produced my Seaman's Identity Card and after taking some of my personal details, she inspected the records and not only confirmed that my friend was a member but even volunteered her home address to me. I couldn't believe my good fortune but, not having actually seen her for over two years, I started to doubt the wisdom of my little adventure into the unknown. I thanked the librarian profusely for her help and set off in the general direction of the address, with a fair deal of apprehension.

I eventually found the address of what turned out to be a flat and parked outside. I'd decided that whilst an immense bunch of flowers might have been a more suitable token to hand her, chocolates could at least be enjoyed by myself, if it turned out that my efforts were in vain. With just one or two butterflies in the proverbial place, I knocked firmly on the door. The look of sheer surprise and disbelief that appeared on her face as she realised who the caller was, was a treat in itself.

'Paul, where the heck have you come from? You're very naughty, you know, just turning up like this without any warning. If you'd come here last night at this time, my boyfriend was here and I don't think he would have been very pleased at all.' Before I had a chance to answer her first question, she continued, 'I see you're in a car. It's yours isn't it? I remember it. Are you working in London now?'

'For heaven's sake, Laura, you've asked me more questions than I'm capable of remembering, so hang on a moment please.'

She burst out laughing. 'You're impossible, Paul, you never change. You just turn up out of the blue and expect me not to be dumbfounded.' There was no stopping her. 'You're sure you've just not run away?' she chided me cheekily.

'Look Laura, if it's not convenient, let me give you this and I'll be on my way.' I handed her my gift, which earned me a kiss on the cheek, and then her hands reached out for mine.

'If you promise not to be naughty, as I know you can be, you're going to have a coffee and tell me what mischief you're getting up to these days.'

'Promise.' I then added rather flippantly, 'You're not expecting your boyfriend tonight, then, I guess.'

'No, Paul, give me credit. Would I have been so daft to invite you in if I were?'

The evening sped by as we caught up on old times and more recent events. Apparently her parents had hoped that I would have rushed her off her feet but she was having nothing of that, either then or now.

'You know, I love my teaching job here and I think a lot about my boyfriend but I do miss home; it hurts sometimes. Why didn't you show your feelings more for me when I was at home?'

'I wish I could answer that. I probably thought you were too good for me and would probably end up losing you to some other guy.'

I guess she realised that wasn't the real reason but she didn't comment further, just nodding her head and looking thoroughly dejected.

113

'Heh, Laura, I didn't come here to make you miserable, for heaven's sake. If you'd like me to get in touch again, of course I will, but I think it's time I was on my way.' I kissed her on her forehead, turned and walked to my car.

'Please take care of yourself,' she blurted out as tears trickled down her flushed cheeks. I knew, at that moment, that she was wishing that I hadn't returned from the past. I'd let my curiosity get the better of me and it had caused her a lot of pain.

The trouble with returning to a vessel after a night ashore on one's own is the assumption by one and all on board that not only have you tripped the light fantastic but also managed to achieve the impossible with the opposite sex. Because of what had happened, I decided that a bit of kidology on this occasion wouldn't go amiss. I certainly wasn't going to be subjected to an inquisition from those who knew it all, or at least claimed to, particularly our Chief Engineer.

He was also not slow to get steamed up about so-called shore repairers who managed to create more problems in the engine room than they'd been called in to resolve. We weren't allowed to do any maintenance work in port ourselves, due to union agreements and demarcation issues, and were very often left at the mercy of unscrupulous operators whose only concern was to get the job done as quickly as possible and then retire to the nearest pub to slake their thirsts. We were invariably left with a monumental job cleaning up the engine room after they had departed and couldn't wait to put things right and back to normal.

On the next voyage, the first in 1962, we had no passengers and therefore feared the worst with the offerings of the Catering Department food-wise. We fully expected that our choice stores would end up being sold abroad by the Chief Steward, with him replacing them with cheap alternative supplies as the vessel had been stored and victualled in anticipation of carrying passengers.

We sailed from London into the teeth of a gale and anchored off Beachy Head in the English Channel, to await an improvement before continuing on passage.

As we headed south the weather improved dramatically, and as

114

we entered the Mediterranean, the Chief was advised that we would be bunkering again at Ceuta despite the successful operation at Messina on the last voyage.

The usual routine of watchkeeping and off-watch socialisation continued, and after a smooth bunkering at Ceuta, we hit heavy weather again on passage to Benghazi. A two-day stopover there was a welcome relief, particularly as we were all invited to a party in the sergeants' mess at the army camp. Recalling my last performance at the same venue, when I had only vague recollections of the evening's events, I was determined to present a more respectable image this time. Well, that was the intention but, like the famous pavements that are paved with gold, hope springs eternal. Our army friends, as usual, were determined that their hospitality should be unforgettable. Regrettably, it was, even more so than last time.

I had just about recovered as we steamed up a flat calm Adriatic Sea to Trieste. It was becoming apparent that our roulette wheel was fast wearing out and at the suggestion of the Chief Engineer, I was delegated to obtain a replacement at a reasonable price. As I'd never previously purchased such an item, Trieste was hardly the best possible place for me to start but, after having a quiet word in the ear of our agent, I eventually managed to achieve a quite remarkable purchase at a bargain price to the amazement of all concerned.

After sailing from Trieste, we had an extremely short stopover at Venice lasting only three hours, before proceeding to Rijeka, where again our stay was for only a few hours.

Messina was our next scheduled port but again of brief duration for only 12 hours before continuing to Palermo. Whilst proceeding round the Sicilian coast and after coming on watch at 8 a.m. it soon became apparent that all was not in order with the main engine. The problems were obviously not only unusual but extremely serious and concerned a serious breakdown of the valve lubrication system.

There was little that we could do to remedy the problems whilst the vessel was under way so there was a desperate requirement to keep the main engine in service until we reached Palermo. By applying liberal quantities of water and oil, mixed to form an emulsion, to the valve parts, we managed to reach Palermo, but by then, the problem had really got out of hand.

The Chief Engineer requested the assistance of shore repair personnel to help us, and in next to no time it seemed as if half of the population of Palermo had decided to come to the vessel out of curiosity; but from amongst this throng emerged a posse of likely lads whose talents would save the day for us. It was necessary to carry out a major dismantling operation in order for the worn-out and damaged parts to be removed ashore for repair where possible, but also some replacement. The repairs proceeded at remarkable speed, with round-the-clock working to suit our requirements, and despite the vast volume of words which our repairers seemed to need to exchange with one another, they demonstrated a great deal of goodwill and humour combined with efficiency. Probably what was more significant was their discovery of the fault that had caused our problems in the first place, which enabled the Chief to come up with a suggestion to avoid trouble in the future.

On completion of the repairs and after the Chief had expressed his satisfaction with them, there then followed what could probably be best described as a light-fingered lottery. Not only were the repairers to receive their just rewards for their efforts but ample recognition was required for the Chief because of his wise choice in using their services. It seemed to me a mighty strange way to cost out the work done, but then I was in no position to query it. The Chief said he would explain the ramifications of his dealings with the repairers but subsequently and conveniently forgot all about it. At that time it looked to me as if the parties called upon to settle the costs were being asked to pay quite a bit more than necessary. It was only much later that I discovered that some repairers are prepared to forfeit part of their profits in order to get work, and one sure way to achieve this was to provide a financial inducement to those who could engage their services.

Our voyage back to the UK was totally uneventful, with not the slightest hint of any repeat of the trouble that had beset us on passage to Palermo, which at least proved the effectiveness of the repairs.

On reflection and after totalling up the sea time I had accumulated to date, the time seemed to be ripe for starting to get together references in preparation for sitting part of my Second Engineer's Certificate of Competency. On approaching the Chief to start the ball rolling, he expressed his willingness to co-operate provided that I prepared it for him to sign. He reckoned that he had more than his fill of paperwork dealing with umpteen additional reporting on top of his usual work because of our problems down below but, in the end and just after we berthed in London, he presented me with the necessary piece of paper, much to my relief.

On reaching London, we were once again greeted with the news that there were no reliefs available. The Chief agreed I could join the daily commuters on the North Kent Line, travelling back and forth between Kent and London and making overnight stopovers at my sister and her family's house. She had invited me to do this previously and, if nothing else, there was a chance to enjoy their company and hospitality, with a welcome change of scenery and people.

The Chief agreed to me using the train rather than my car because of the London traffic delays and he required me to appear on time each day with no excuses for being late due, but after three days of performing with the early morning rat race of London-bound commuters, I was more than grateful for the weekend break. I looked in amazement at their antics as they boarded the train each morning carrying not only the obligatory carefully rolled umbrella, briefcase and *Financial Times* but, bless their souls, a folding camping stool each on which to park their backsides. British Rail were as close then as subsequently to having to admit to defeat when it came to carrying a high passenger load on seats at peak traffic periods.

After my commuting experiences, I decided that that life wouldn't be for me, a decision with which my brother-in-law totally agreed, and he was a man of Kent. Nevertheless I had enjoyed the change and shared the company of family I thought the world of.

As the time drew near for our next departure from London, we were advised that, once again, there would be no passengers boarding. Our first thoughts, as usual, turned to the likely degeneration of the Catering Department's offerings to us food-wise, but the first few days of the voyage passed smoothly enough with nothing unusual happening and I decided it was high time I got down to some studying if I intended sitting examinations in the not too distant future.

As it turned out, the food was almost passable whichever way you looked at it, but with the weather starting to deteriorate as we headed further south, both the offerings from the Catering Department and the studying suffered a similar fate, a marked reduction in both quantity and quality. It was becoming almost a necessity to steal into the galley after coming off watch at midnight, with the purpose of cooking a premature breakfast, a practise which the Chief totally approved of but was guaranteed to mess up the Chief Steward's victualling schedules. I didn't feel at all guilty about performing in the galley for a short while after hours, so to speak. The fact that we had to have keys to access the cold stores because of the refrigeration equipment played no small part in our ability to plunder the breakfast stores.

The weather deteriorated even more as we headed along the North African coast towards Malta, then, as if out of the blue, a four-engined bomber appeared overhead on our course and heading, reminding us once again of the previous unnerving experience we had gone through. We rushed out onto the deck, staring upwards with the vain hope of trying to identify the nationality, and were greeted with the sight of flares dropping into the sea around us. We just prayed and hoped that we were being used solely for targeting practice, although there was precious little we could do if we weren't. I later found out that the airwaves were blue as the Captain had tried to communicate with the airborne lunatics but to no avail.

We were not at all sorry to berth in Valletta harbour in order to discharge our cargo of potatoes. The grand scale of the harbour, the city walls, the massive guns and buildings, leaves one not at all surprised that the British Mediterranean Fleet were based here for so long.

Unfortunately we were not berthed at a quay but were lying anchored with our stern mooring ropes attached to mooring buoys, which meant that getting ashore required some form of waterborne transport and this was not readily available.

The Second Mate then decided to let us into a very well-kept secret. With us having no passengers, he'd apparently approached the Captain about having a party on board at Valletta and inviting the Wrens stationed there. The fact that his sister-in-law was a Wren in residence in Malta turned out to be a winning card and the Captain agreed, subject not only to him being invited but also that no damage was caused to the passenger areas, and the Catering Department were not expected to have to contribute their services.

The Second Engineer offered to run the bar and with his undoubted knowledge on alcohol related matters, this seemed to be an excellent idea. The Stewardess, who'd been having a holiday of her own, volunteered to prepare the party titbits, and there was no shortage of ideas as to what the entertainment should consist of, provided of course, the Captain approved. Promptly at 2000 hours that evening, a naval launch arrived alongside and disembarked a party of Wrens on board, the launch departing with a shouted warning that they would return at 2400 hours prompt to collect our guests but would not hang around for any malingerers.

I suppose I'm not a lot different to many people when it comes to trying to recollect just what happened at a party, particularly if one's a little inebriated, and this party was no exception. Suffice to say that I recall a mish mash of mental flashes, some good, some not so good and some decidedly debilitating.

The decision by us all to agree to the Second Engineer running the bar turned out to be not a very clever one at all. His ideas on what constituted a cocktail were certainly not compatible with either accepted bar practice or maintaining anything akin to a clear head, a steady gait and the undivided attention of any of our guests.

In retrospect, it looked as if he had decided in advance, to influence the outcome of the party by destroying the opposition, so to speak. Even the Captain was caught out by the Second's strategic planning just as he appeared to be making grand overtures to the Second Mate's sister-in-law. In any event, whatever the Second Engineer may or may not have had in mind, it was most unlikely that he could have planned for the Captain not only to be the first

119

to disgrace himself but also to break the very rules he himself had insisted on being complied with.

It must be said, though, that the sight of the Captain trying to do a backwards somersault whilst sat in a chair, gin in hand, will forever remain etched in not only my memory but, no doubt those of a few more who were present to witness this remarkable spectacle.

It was my turn next. I was only trying to be a gentleman and get the lady a drink, but on the way back from the bar and when almost on the point of handing her the drink, my legs decided to go on strike and not support the rest of me, with the result that the glass, closely followed by its contents, found their way, like guided missiles, to their unintended targets which included parts of her body that did not need reviving. I then did my cause no good at all by trying to recover the situation from the lounge carpet. That wasn't very clever at all and I literally crawled away to bury my head in shame.

Just great, I was thinking to myself as I collapsed into my cabin chair, when several of our guests appeared from nowhere at my open door. They'd decided that the Second Engineer had to be fixed, once and for all. Four of their own party whose drinking capabilities were proven beyond doubt had also succumbed to his shenanigans. Their plan was simple. They were going to entice him onto the launch and, once ashore, abandon him to his fate, with there being no chance of a lift back to the vessel at that time of the night.

The only problem that I could see with their plan, as I struggled to explain to the girls, was that the Second Engineer was, in all probability, stone-cold sober and therefore unlikely to fall for their proposal. They decided there and then that if that were the case then it was time for them to change his state of sobriety.

They disappeared as quickly as they had appeared. Only next day, after I'd partially recovered from the Second's alcoholic aberrations, did I discover what had apparently transpired later that night. I was told that I'd missed a song and dance routine presented by our guests that would not have disgraced the Television Toppers, despite the fragile state they were in. This was followed by a jolly party piece prepared by the Second Mate and the stewardess, with a final face-saving appearance by the

Captain, who had made a dramatic recovery and decided it was time to call it a day, but with a drink on him all round to bid the Wrens farewell.

15

Our next port was Benghazi as usual but then came a change in our usual routine. We were to proceed to Kalamata and then to Ayienta in the Gulf of Corinth, to load currants, followed by a voyage up the Adriatic to Rijeka before returning to Malta to load cargo for the UK.

Our stays at both Kalamata and Ayienta were both relatively of short duration and with our watches being maintained at Ayienta, I decided to take a stroll ashore in the afternoon after lunch. Nobody else seemed the slightest bit interested in going, although that was probably not too surprising because we seemed to be berthed in the middle of the countryside, miles from anywhere, with the mountains stretching as far as the eye could see.

A ship, whether at sea or in port, is never quiet despite the usually relaxed atmosphere in the accommodation spaces and I was more than amply reminded of this as I stepped ashore, cleared the jetty and headed off, hopefully in the general direction towards habitation. The peace, quiet and tranquillity of that remote country lane seemed too good to be true. It was just as if life was standing still, with neither sight or sound of any human being for miles. In the distance, it was just possible to discern a vineyard and as I drew nearer, my eyes caught sight of the most immense clusters of fleshy blue-black grapes, with the vine leaves being as green as green could possibly be.

I remembered feeling just the same when on visits deep in the heart of the Yorkshire Dales and whilst reflecting on these memories, my thoughts were abruptly interrupted by the staccato back-firing of a motor scooter that roared past me, driven by a young man who was obviously trying to impress his female companion sitting sideways on the saddle yet somehow managing to stay on board.

I wandered on and reached a small settlement, complete with the mandatory café, outside tables and old men with dogs that had seen better days. Despite the colours of the rainbow and the advantage of wearing light-coloured clothing to reflect the sun's burning rays, the only colours evident amongst the natives' clothing were black and blue. Yet on the opposite side of the Mediterranean, the chances of seeing any black or blue garments being worn by the North Africans was just about nil, with white being the predominant choice.

Fortunately, buying a glass of wine doesn't require much linguistic capability and I joined the locals, feeling about as comfortable as Count Dracula at a garden party.

It is said that time stands still in certain places and this place certainly seemed at a standstill. I could have been on another planet, yet the ship was moored only a mile or so away.

After enjoying a further glass of the local brew, it was time to make my way slowly and reluctantly back to reality, inhaling the rich sweet smells of the country air, deep into my lungs.

I'd only been back on board a few minutes when the Chief reminded me of a matter which should have been uppermost in my mind.

'Fourth, have you remembered to write to the company requesting a relief at the end of this voyage? If you haven't, you'd better get your finger out because your letter will have to be posted at the next port, otherwise you won't have given them sufficient notice.'

'Thanks for the reminder, Chief. No, I haven't written yet but I'll do that on the way to Rijeka.'

Like so many intentions and with numerous other pressing commitments, I only eventually managed to get my letter written at the last minute on the day of our departure from Rijeka.

'Are you going ashore before the vessel sails, Paul?' asked the Radio Officer.

He had a telepathic sense of knowing how to get someone else to do his running around for him. This time it was a letter he wanted posting. His idea of exercise, apart from that with the opposite sex, was an appearance on deck for a breath of fresh air.

123

'Yes, I suppose so. I'll see if there are any more for posting.'

As I approached the gangway to go ashore, the Second Mate called out. 'Paul, don't forget that shore leave expires in, let's see, just over an hour.'

'Thanks, Dave, I'm only going as far as the post office. Shouldn't be more than half an hour.'

It's a pity that the Second Mate hadn't reminded me about making sure I didn't have any foreign currency on my person. There again, if I'd remembered to glance at my shore pass, I would have been reminded that 'Every misdemeanour will be persecuted'. Probably that is exactly what they meant but, in any case, that warning might just have been enough to remind me to check my pockets.

It was a glorious sunny afternoon with a gentle breeze, ideal for walking and as I passed the armed guard at the harbour exit gate, showing my pass, I couldn't resist a friendly grin, which produced the usual bland response.

Plenty of time, I thought; only 15 minutes' stroll to the post office then a wander around the square and back to the vessel in three-quarters of an hour. I hadn't any intention of making any purchases so after posting the mail and enjoying my pleasant and relaxing stroll and congratulating myself on getting ashore just one more time before sailing, I headed back to the harbour entrance.

'Stop! Stop!'

The command brought me abruptly to a standstill and sharply to my senses.

'Step this way,' the guard demanded.

'Hey,' I said, 'What the hell's going on? I'm just returning to my ship after posting some letters.'

'You will come with me,' said the guard.

I didn't argue. I was marched away from the harbour, down a side street to a very drab-looking multistorey building.

'This way,' the guard ordered.

By now, I was feeling more than decidedly uneasy.

'Up the stairs,' he persisted.

I couldn't find fault with the guard's command of English. I was led into a room, into the presence of a uniformed official sprouting

124

more gold braid than could possibly be good for me. He glared in my direction.

'What is going on?' I asked.

'You will answer my questions but first you will empty the pockets of your clothing, then you will step back two paces,' he responded.

My God, I thought. I remembered I hadn't bothered to check that I had only Yugoslavian money on me before stepping ashore. Money, mainly in note form and in a variety of denominations, tumbled onto the table.

'What is the meaning of this?' he remonstrated. 'You have abused our laws.'

'For heaven's sake,' I pleaded. 'Let me explain. I only came ashore to post some letters, not to spend any money. I've only been ashore for a short while – your guard at the exit gate will confirm that.'

'First, you will complete these forms then I will question you,' he replied.

I glanced at the questions. 'Oh, no, sorry,' I said. 'I require the British Consul and the ship's Captain. In fact, I should be back on board by now as we are due to sail very shortly.'

'You will not be sailing anywhere if you do not complete these forms,' he commanded.

I was then handed three forms; the first required me to divulge personal details about myself and my family, the second required details of my job and the company I worked for and finally I was required to disclose where I had obtained the money and the amounts and denominations involved. My first reaction was to refuse to disclose any of the information they demanded, but then fortunately I had a flash of inspiration.

'If I complete these forms, will you allow me to rejoin my ship?' I asked.

'Yes, but that will have to be agreed with the Port Master,' the official replied.

Trying not to give even a hint of the utter and complete balderdash I was writing, I quickly answered the questions and handed over the forms, with a good deal more than butterflies in my stomach. I knew I would not get my money back but that seemed a

125

small price to pay for my freedom. After studying the forms and muttering among themselves, probably about how they were going to share their ill-gotten gains, I was led out of the room, down the stairs and back to the harbour to await my fate. I did not have long to wait. The telephone rang, the guard spoke briefly, then with a final warning from the guard that every misdemeanour perpetrated by me would be persecuted, he waved me on my way.

'Sure thing,' I replied. Of that I had little doubt. I sped back to the vessel as fast as my legs would allow me and arrived breathless on board.

I literally bumped into the Third Mate on entering the accommodation.

'Where the hell have you been, Paul? The Old Man is going spare. We should have sailed three-quarters of an hour ago.'

'You'll never believe this Alan,' I gasped, struggling to recover my breath.

I briefly recounted my ordeal before reporting to the Captain, who fortunately accepted that I was the innocent victim of my own stupidity and as it was hopefully my last voyage on the vessel, he considered that no further action was required to be taken by him. I think he was simply relieved to see me safely back on board in one piece.

I still haven't been back to Yugoslavia and now, after all the unpleasant things that have subsequently happened, I don't suppose I ever will.

One can't but help feeling a great deal of sadness for a nation that could only find in itself the power to swap the dark, drab, unimaginative and mentally threatening days of yesteryear for a vicious, cruel and physically punitive regime supposedly in the name of freedom of thought and expression. Why oh why can't they accept that a meaningful existence on this planet has little to do with what can be plundered, destroyed or browbeaten from human beings but is more related to using to the best of their ability the God-given natural and human attributes that they, as a country, are so well endowed with.

On our passage down the Adriatic Sea, the weather was not at all kind, with gale force winds and heavy seas, and this situation did not change to any extent before we reached Malta. As I was not on watch approaching Valletta, I took the opportunity to admire the view but ended up admiring the proficiency of the pilot in guiding us through the difficult channel approach into the harbour in the testing weather conditions.

Once again I was truly impressed with the scale of the infrastructure and the backdrop of Valletta and its surrounds. After surviving my close call in Rijeka and with this being the last port in the Mediterranean, I decided to throw caution to the winds and suggested to the Chief Engineer that I hire a car and we go for a grand tour of Malta. This way I could not draw the short straw with one of us having to stay behind to literally man the pumps. As it was not costing the Chief a penny, he readily agreed. The Third Engineer was the unfortunate person who was going to have to remain on board.

What really surprised me was the relative ease that one could hire a car in Valletta, also the cheapness, and after signing all the necessary forms and obtaining a road map, we sped off in search of Utopia – or the next best thing. Nevertheless, I was determined to try and avoid our trip becoming the Maltese equivalent of a British pub crawl, with me having to stay relatively sober in my capacity as chauffeur. My intention was to get clear of Valletta as soon as possible and head off towards the hotel complexes on the coast which were said to have all the latest facilities for holiday enjoyment.

Not for the first time, the good intentions didn't stand up to the light of day. We were not proposing to spend a fortune both in time and money on a gambling run that commenced in the first hotel complex we stopped off at. The Chief, however, seemed intent on trying to recover the losses he'd incurred on board and at first it looked as if his gamble was paying off, until his luck turned sour on him and his profits dwindled rapidly to the point where we had to drag him away from the tables, otherwise we would be pawning the car to pay off his debts.

The Second Engineer was a little more successful with his gambling and, for a change, it looked as if I might threaten to be making a profit. On the strict understanding that we would treat him to a meal if he refrained from any further gambling, the Chief agreed to just sit and watch our efforts. The effort he was making to stick to his side of the bargain was obviously becoming too much of a strain, so after receiving our winnings, we proceeded on our way to a new location on the other side of the island, which had been recommended to us as one of the best eating establishments in the area.

Our meal and wine turned out to be a deliciously rewarding experience which improved the Chief's mood no end. Driving around the island was an effortless exercise, unbelievably smooth and enjoyable, there being so little traffic that one had the roads virtually to oneself.

After returning the car to the hirers in one piece, it was suggested that our shore trip would not be complete without a trip to the Gut in downtown Valletta. What the Gut has is a superabundance of nightlife, with a promise of better things to come – or that, at least, appears to be the case. It's a focal point for seamen of many nationalities from both naval and merchant ships, who congregate in the bars to down their drinks in the company of the local females.

And that is where the major problem exists because, as on the night we were there, both the American and British navies were in harbour in addition to the merchantmen. It usually doesn't take too long for the alcohol consumption levels to make their presences felt mainly in the guise of feverish nationalistic claims. Simply having a good time and enjoying themselves ashore is never enough, so inevitably war breaks out. In our presence, it was alleged by our own naval compatriots that the American naval lads left a lot to be desired particularly with regard to their appreciation of the local talent.

Unfortunately for the participants, the Maltese police are dab hands at dealing with trouble in the Gut, together with the MPs from both navies, and the troublemakers were soon rounded up, the only losses being a fair quantity of wine, beer and glasses and not a little blood.

It seems surprising that merchant vessels crews don't generally suffer the same problems as their naval compatriots, probably due to better self-discipline. The Gut had not really been a big surprise to me, the girls promising far more than what was really on offer, working hand in glove with the bar owners to maximise their profits.

Lovelife or no lovelife, one matter that was becoming urgent was the fast disappearing time left for me to get down to study if I was going to get any further promotion. It was not absolutely certain that I would get relieved on our return to London; in fact, based on the previous voyages of late, there was a fair chance that there would be no relief available. With the crew on board, it was not at all easy to concentrate on any study in off-watch hours, with plenty of tales and anecdotes emanating from one and all, not least the Third Engineer, whose true love of the moment a BOAC air hostess, was still flying on Comets to the Far East. Life would almost certainly have been a lot easier for them if they hadn't spent so much time passing one another in opposite directions and at vastly different altitudes. There seemed little doubt at all that if they could only manage to remain in the same place long enough, they would get hitched.

The Second Engineer had had a complicated life so far, with his earlier years having been spent in the Royal Navy before leaving to join the Merchant Navy. His enthusiasm and zest for life was almost as incredible as his sense of humour. Looking back now, I can hardly remember a time when he was other than at peace with life despite the horrors that sometimes beset shipboard life, particularly in the engine room.

The Chief Engineer's zest for life was almost as large as the Second's and Third's except that in his case food overrode all other considerations, therefore none of us could imagine the Chief getting hitched unless his intended had special virtues in this direction.

The Second Mate spent almost all his waking hours missing his bedmate, talking about little else so we couldn't wait to meet this voluptuous female when the ship berthed in London.

The Mate was looking forward to his next ship as he had been promised what was, more or less, promotion to the company's flagship.

The Third Mate had spent the first part of the voyage trying to work out his chances of succeeding where others had failed.

She was a Gina Lollobrigida lookalike and was the company's agent's daughter at Trieste. The agent, originally from England, had married an Italian lady and between them they had produced a stunningly beautiful lass, to say the least. She had a reputation of playing very hard to get but, having lived in Italy most of her life, that was very understandable. The Captain had warned us all a long time previously not to play with fire if we valued our jobs with the company, this young lady being simply far too hot to handle. The warning had fallen on deaf ears as far as the Third Mate was concerned; in fact, it had been more of a challenge to him. Now, on our way back to the UK, he continuously referred to his misfortune in not establishing a liaison with her. None of us had the heart to tell him he'd probably have more chance winning the football pools.

The Captain made no secret of the fact that he was looking forward to a holiday with his wife in Scotland, so there was no doubt at all we were all wishing the days away until we berthed in London.

The weather didn't deteriorate on this voyage too badly, and with relatively routine watchkeeping, the days were passing smoothly by, but it was with a feeling of mixed emotions that I realised I would probably be leaving the vessel and crew very soon. Then a short leave before going back to college for study prior to sitting the examinations necessary for promotion.

Once again, as we steamed up the English Channel, the green fields and countryside almost leapt out into mid-channel to greet us and welcome us home.

On berthing in London, the reliefs were actually on board as the gangway went down, and in no time we were homeward-bound, without delay for once.

One of the problems of sharing a car with other family members is the frustration when the car disappears to the other end of the country for an indefinite period, as mine had just done. They had got used to the availability of my car whilst I was away and there was an urgent need for me to acquire another vehicle if I wasn't to be left with only my motorbike for transport. I also needed suitable transport to attend college each day, and turning up in soaking wet outer garments is no way to endear yourself to the college authorities. After much thought and consideration, I decided to take a gamble on purchasing a second-hand Sunbeam Alpine Sports Coupé which had been entered in several car rallies with some success on occasions. The price being asked was too tempting for me to turn down and despite warnings from my family about buying a pig in a poke, I became the proud owner of what was undoubtedly a head-turning car and more than just a little likely to provide me with transport to attract the opposite sex.

I didn't have too long to wait to discover I was going to have to acknowledge that owning such a car could result in unexpected encounters with complete strangers. I had been attending college for several weeks during a prolonged transport strike and had been taking my father into the city each morning so he could get to work. He was working part-time only, being well past normal retirement age, and he managed to get a lift home each afternoon, which left my one and only passenger seat vacant for my homeward-bound journey. I was crawling along in heavy traffic eastbound from the city when I was forced to a stop by the traffic ahead. No sooner had I stopped than my passenger door opened and in dropped the most delectable dolly that one could imagine. I was speechless – but she wasn't.

'You don't mind, do you? I'd be most grateful if you could drop me off about a couple of miles down the road. I'm absolutely worn out and late.'

'Not at all,' I replied. 'What's made you so tired, if you don't mind me asking?'

It turned out she was a sales demonstrator in a showroom but was also expected to visit other premises, and that was just where she was heading.

My college studies were not very demanding as I was going over ground that I had previously covered for examinations before my seagoing career, so this gave me the opportunity to catch up with my social life. A very good friend from my school days had recently returned from service in the Bermuda Police Force, after previously serving in the Coldstream Guards and the Northern Rhodesia Police Force. Not only was he keen on car-rallying but

131

he had a tremendous zest for life and equipped himself with an MGB Sports Coupé which he alleged was vastly superior to a Sunbeam Alpine.

As far as the girl-friends were concerned they didn't seem at all impressed by the fact that my car had wire wheels or a Borg Warner overdrive, or that my friend's car, being much newer, had all the latest gadgetry available for sports cars. They were just happy to be sharing an evening with two guys lucky enough to be able to afford the cars in question and the entertainment to go with it.

As my car had something of a rally history, I was persuaded, against my better judgement, to enter a well-known northern rally, with my friend as navigator. Despite my previous experience of rallies, rallying had moved on a fair way since my last involvement, so instead of just being required to stay on the chosen route, not exceed statutory speed limits and maintain arrivals and departures from checkpoints within fairly close limits, there suddenly loomed the threat of secret checkpoints, timed sections and even special stages which, until then, had only appeared in foreign rallies.

Blissfully unaware of what we were truly letting ourselves in for, we headed off literally into the unknown. A 300-mile overnight rally extending into the Yorkshire Dales and Moors was always going to be overambitious without plenty of practice, particularly as my friend's understanding of the navigator's duties for this particular rally was extremely dubious. In his opinion it would all be a piece of cake, with my driving skills and his navigation skills being a force too powerful for the competition.

It was only after two of the competitors had passed us travelling in the opposite direction that matters came to a head.

'Silly buggers, Paul. What the hell do they think they are playing at? Frightened the living daylights out of me. How about you?'

'Geoff, has it occurred to you that those cars could be going in the right direction? Let's face it, one car going the wrong way is possible but surely not two.'

'It's a well-known fact in rallying, that if in doubt, follow the car in front.'

'I just hope you are right for your sake, buddy,' I replied, knowing full well that he was bluffing.

Within minutes we were approaching the next checkpoint from the wrong direction, which meant immediate disqualification. We agreed that if we ever entered another rally, preparation would be the keyword and we would put this debacle down to experience.

Geoff had a long-time female admirer who was more than anxious to have him for her own. Unfortunately for her, he was not ready to have his colours nailed to the mast, or something less painful, and this did not please her at all. It just so happened that I rather fancied her myself although she had not shown similar interest in me. A grand plan came into my head. I suggested to Geoff that I invite her to join me on a trip to my sister's in Kent and, providing she accepted, he could claim she no longer put him in the number one spotlight. I also intended to suggest to her that by accepting my invitation, she would make Geoff insanely jealous of me and he would be quick to realise that he might lose her.

Whether it was by good luck or good fortune, I didn't establish, but both parties accepted my plan and in no time we were speeding off to Kent. The big mistake I made was to believe that she might just change her attitude to me on holiday. She was full of gaiety, friendliness and fun but strictly on a platonic basis; then it dawned that I'd had the tables turned on me. By the time we were homeward-bound, I was in a state of utter frustration, having been denied the opportunity to express my feelings for her. It seemed therefore a good idea not to dilly-dally on the way, and as the car was capable of a speed in excess of a ton, could a high-speed run warm the cockles of her heart, or any other appropriate parts?

Just when I thought that my new strategy was beginning to pay off, disaster struck, due to a moment's lack of concentration on my part.

'Paul, may I ask why are we trailing a smokescreen?' She sounded very concerned.

I had approached the Norman Cross roundabout on the A1 at around 90 m.p.h. in overdrive top gear, and as I dropped down through the gears, somehow momentarily forgot the overdrive and skipped a gear, thereby over-revving the engine into the red sector. If the engine had not been previously exploited in its rally days, it might well have accepted this unfortunate happening with good grace.

'I have literally put my foot in it, Jacqueline, probably blown a piston or the rings at least.'

We still had a fair journey ahead of us, and as my finances would not stand further assault, I decided to try and limp home at a crawl.

Surprisingly, she accepted our misfortune with good grace and, despite the accompanying thick, black pall of smoke that trailed us for miles, managed to try and pretend it was nothing to do with us.

During the long slow crawl home, I reflected on what to say to her as parting words. In the end, she persuaded me to kid Geoff that we'd had a terrific time, and I promised her I would.

'Geoff, I'm not sure you'll be all that pleased when I tell you this. Jacqueline and I had a terrific holiday. In fact, we almost blew a gasket,' I suggested.

'Hope that will teach you to try harder next time you're trying to pinch a guy's girlfriend.'

We roared with laughter. I doubted very much whether our mutual friend would have seen things in quite the same way.

16

I suppose there was little chance that being appointed Fourth Engineer on the company's top vessel in the fleet would not attract some sarcastic comments about what one had done to achieve this recognition. Yet, for my part and after sweating it out for over a year down the Mediterranean, the new appointment could not have come at a better time. The thought of spending almost one week berthed in Gothenburg in Sweden and the other week in one's home port seemed almost too good to be true. I liked to think that the company had recognised my success in passing the first part of my Second Class Certificate of Competency for Steamships following my attendance at college but the appointment was more likely the result of my availability at the required time.

After several weeks of leave following my departure from the *Leo* and then a spell of relieving duty, I was looking forward to exercising my sea legs once again. Unfortunately my car engine required to be completely dismantled to carry out the necessary repairs and neither time or money had allowed me to do so. It looked as if the car would be remaining immobile for a lengthy period and I reflected on the warnings I'd received about purchasing such a car with a background of hard rallying. I'd been forced onto two wheels once again and, despite my love for motorcycling, they never quite provided the same intimate means of conveyance as their four-wheeled counterparts. One can hardly enjoy a cosy evening nosh with one's girlfriend in some downtown eating house when, at the back of your mind, is the prospect of having to dress for the Arctic conditions and gale force winds trying their best to flatten the establishment one's occupying.

Had summer been in the offing, then these thoughts would not have been passing through my mind but it was now late autumn and, as far as I was concerned, it was time for my two-wheeled machine to go into hibernation.

It was only shortly after boarding the *Lara* that I was given a sharp reminder of the difference in standards applicable on this vessel as opposed to the previous ones I had sailed on.

'You're the new Fourth Engineer then,' boomed a voice down the alleyway.

I spun round to face a large, red-haired uniformed gentleman wearing four gold braid rings on his epaulettes.

'Yes, Captain, I'm very pleased to meet you,' I answered.

'Right then, I just want you to be aware at the outset, young man, that you won't be wandering around this vessel in a boiler suit or in your shirtsleeves. Neither will you swear in the presence of the passengers, drink excessively or enter the passenger accommodation or public areas on the upper decks unless you are required to carry out repairs, in which case you must obtain prior permission from the Chief Steward and Stewardess.'

I hesitated before answering to make sure he'd completed his orders.

'Yes, Captain, I fully understand what you say. I must say I really am looking forward to sailing on your vessel,' I replied.

'There's no need to be sarcastic, Fourth,' he boomed, and then departed forthwith.

'You've met the Old Man,' said the Chief. 'He may seem to be full of a bit more than his own importance, Fourth, and a little bit round the bend, but his wartime service made sure he's entered the history books,' he added with due reverence.

I couldn't help but be aware of the difference between the calm, sincere and considerate approach of the Chief Engineer and the authoritative, almost overbearing attitude of the Captain, obviously well ingrained in the oil and water syndrome.

The Chief came over to me on first impressions as a true English gentleman and, in all probability, a first-class engineer and human being in most respects. After all, he was the company's Commodore Chief Engineer.

'Well, Chief, I suppose it takes all types, so to speak, but it's a pleasure to meet you and I'll do my best not to let you or the department down. I can assure you that after what seemed a never-ending spell down the Mediterranean, I'm in no hurry to want to leave this vessel.'

'Fourth, you've got excellent Second and Third Engineers and the Mates are also a decent bunch, so all in all, provided you keep your nose clean, you should be around for quite a while. Your pre-decessor was here for at least nine months and was promoted on leaving,' the Chief added.

At least it looked to me as if the Chief was not insisting on get-ting his pound of flesh from us all in order to retain his position as the company's senior seagoing engineer. What I didn't realise was that this vessel's trading pattern to Scandinavia allowed more than ample time in port to not only keep well up to date with all opera-tional and maintenance requirements but to live a bit of the life of O'Reilly. The Chief had no cause whatsoever to chase us work-wise and this was new for me.

'By the way, Fourth, I'm told you're a single man. Is that cor-rect?' asked the Chief.

'That's perfectly true, but, who knows, I might meet the girl of my dreams on board,' I replied.

'Well, if you do,' added the Third Engineer, 'you better not let the Old Man catch you, eh Chief? Us engineers are not considered suitable acquaintances for the female passengers.'

'What you've just said, Third, has a familiar ring about it but that was some time ago on another ship and with another captain,' I said in a reflective mood.

The Third Engineer was a young married man with three chil-dren, who would have given his left leg to stay on the vessel, but he knew, because he'd been there well over a year, that it would soon be time to move on. He also knew that in all probability there was the likelihood his next vessel would result in him being away from home for considerably longer periods of time.

It was also becoming increasingly apparent to me that what I'd been told about the Captain was quite true. He certainly had an aura of grandeur more befitting the Cunard Line and one of the *Queens*. As the days passed, it was also obvious that many of the passengers were suitably impressed by his demeanour, but not all.

137

It was Sunday afternoon, we were well over halfway across the North Sea with perfect sea conditions when suddenly it seemed that life was all in a spin, literally.

There was a knock on my cabin door. A somewhat bewildered old gentleman enquired if I could help him to decide whether he was going barmy or, alternatively, what he thought was happening was actually happening.

'Fourth, I have been out on deck for nearly half an hour and the ruddy ship seems to be going round in circles. Surely that can't be right?' he queried.

'Really,' I said. 'You're not being serious, are you?'

'I most certainly am,' he replied almost indignantly.

'To be perfectly honest with you, I haven't been out on deck since lunchtime but I'll certainly investigate right away on your behalf,' I promised.

I did, and returned.

'You're quite right; no doubt about it. We're making rings around something or other but I don't know what as yet,' I reported.

I didn't wish to disturb the Chief or the Second Engineer, who would be having their post-lunch naps, so I slipped down below to see the Third Engineer.

'What brings you below, Fourth?' enquired the Third.

'It looks as if we've been going round in bloody circles for quite a while and this passenger gent has just asked me to explain why. Do you know?' I queried.

'Just the Old Man having a spin, I expect. Nothing new in that. Seems to do it for kicks. He gets the Second Mate and the watch-keepers off the bridge, the cadet to lash the wheel in the hard over position and then says his prayers doing circles at full speed. That's the truth, so help me God,' the Third added.

'How the hell does he get away with it?' I asked. 'Surely the company must get some queries from the passengers,' I added.

'He's been doing these things for years, apparently. He probably tells the company that he's been having trouble with the navigation equipment and is swinging the vessel to check the DF bearings and the compasses etcetera.'

I returned to deck and tried to sound convincing but I was pretty sure that the passenger gent had already decided we were all crackers.

'You mean to say that it is necessary to go round in circles in the middle of the North Sea, to put things right?' he persisted, looking extremely perplexed.

'Well,' I rejoined, 'We're hardly likely to collide with another vessel out here, are we?'

'No, I suppose not, but you know, young man, I've been travelling on ships for over fifty years and I've never witnessed a performance like this before.'

It wasn't too long before I did meet the girl of my dreams. Elaine had been on holiday in Sweden staying with a friend near Stockholm and she seemed not the least bit surprised when I invited her to join me for drinks in my cabin.

We chatted about her holiday, which was her first visit to Sweden. She told me she was a teacher, lived in Lancashire and then, after sensing that I was single, asked me how many girl-friends I'd had.

'Quite a few until now, Elaine,' I grinned, in reply.

'Oh, come off it, Paul. We've only just met and you're falling in love with me.' She smiled broadly and breathed deeply.

'Am I? Well, what's wrong with that? You can't help looking like a dish and smelling like "heaven on earth".' I had to admit I was going over the top, in the nicest possible way, but I couldn't help myself.

There was a loud repeated knocking on my cabin door.

'What the hell now?' I murmured.

The knocking was repeated but more urgently than before. I got up and opened the door, to be confronted by the Stewardess looking quite agitated.

'Would I be right in thinking that you have Elaine in your cabin, Fourth?' she enquired.

'I can't deny that,' I said. 'Just having a chat, you know. No harm in that, surely.'

'The Captain wishes to see you immediately in his office,' she persisted.

'Sorry, Elaine, it looks as if I'm in trouble, one way or another.'

'What, over me seeing you here? You have got to be joking,' Elaine was not only staggered by this development but obviously extremely unhappy.

'Please say no more, young woman,' the Stewardess advised. 'The Captain does not allow passengers to enter cabins which are not on the passenger decks, without his permission.'

I made my way up to the Captain's office and knocked on his door.

'Who's that?' the familiar booming voice reverberated around the upper deck.

'Fourth Engineer, sir.'

'Step in here right away, young man. Is it true that you have been entertaining a young female passenger in your cabin?' He wasn't joking. His hair seemed even redder than ever with his face an even deeper shade.

'Just chatting, Captain, nothing more,' I pleaded.

'And what did I warn you of when you joined my vessel?' he thundered.

'Yes, I know, sir, but surely to God—'

'Don't you dare use the Lord's name in vain in my presence or I'll have your guts for garters.' By now sweat was pouring off his brow and his face was as red as it could possibly be.

A deep sense of foreboding overcame me. It looked as if my stay on this fine vessel was going to be extremely short-lived, if the Captain had his way. He calmed down, reached for a glass of water, took a long slow drink, then mopped his brow with an enormous white handkerchief almost the size of a table napkin.

'Right, Fourth, I think I have made myself absolutely clear this time, so take this as a final warning from me. If you repeat this behaviour you will be reported to the company and sent packing. Do you understand me?'

'Yes, sir, thanks, sir, no doubt at all.'

I backpedalled out of his office, nearly falling backwards as I tripped over the door sill, and then somehow or other managed to avoid knocking a drinks tray out of the Second Steward's hands.

'How bad was it, Paul?' Her voice startled me, coming appar-

140

ently from nowhere as I stood in the darkness in a quiet corner of the after deck, trying to regain my composure after the Captain's dressing down.

'Not too bad really, I suppose. Threatened me with a big heave-ho and will probably cut my tongue off if I speak to you again,' I replied. 'It's just like the Third Reich. In fact I reckon I will nick-name our Stewardess The Fräulein,' I joked.

'He must be insanely jealous of you, you know. What the hell gets into the heads of some middle-aged men, I just don't know. It was just the same in Sweden, in fact even worse. I was pestered by men old enough to be my grandfather. They just don't know when to lay off us females.'

'Elaine, it's great to hear what you think but it isn't the first time I've come across this problem. When I was on the Western Ocean run, just after I started my seagoing career, exactly the same thing happened,' I added.

'Well, you shouldn't go chasing after all the Captain's girls,' she gently chided.

She was making me wish I could just simply whisk her off the vessel away from the ever prying eyes and spying vendettas of The Fräulein, who was obviously in collusion with the Old Man.

'I just don't know, Elaine, I think we'd better play it cool until the end of the voyage.'

'Oh, come on, you surely aren't going to let that old witch get the better of you, she's probably getting a handsome backhander from the Captain to spy on you.'

'Yes, I suppose you are right,' I said.

'Look, Paul, I can't see that old biddy being around much after midnight, so after you've come off watch and had your shower, shall I sneak down to your cabin?'

My knees felt like jelly. Here I was being virtually proposi-tioned by a voluptuous female and the only thing I could think of was that bloody knocking on my cabin door and The Fräulein's unfriendly face. Oh, hell, in for a penny in for a pound. I could always march an Alsatian around the perimeter of an airfield if the worst came to the worst.

'That sounds just fine by me, but can I suggest that instead of coming by the obvious route to my cabin, you take a devious route and approach our accommodation from aft? Can I also suggest that you make up your bed to look as if you're in it? I wouldn't put it past the old witch to check your cabin as she has a pass-key to all passenger cabins so she can enter even if you lock it.'

Even the donkeyman on my watch couldn't help but notice that my mind was more on other matters than the routine watch keeping duties.

'If I didn't know you better, Fourth, I'd say you've got problems with a woman.'

'Good heavens, what on earth makes you think that, Donks?' I volunteered, as light-heartedly as I could.

Even the ruddy crew were becoming involved in my amorous adventures. What next?

The watch seemed interminable. I kept thinking about Elaine then the old witch and couldn't help but imagine the worst happening. Was I about to enter heaven or hell?

The Third Engineer came on watch.

'I'm not totally in the dark, Paul. Get to it, lad, she's a cracker. How about taking my cabin, otherwise The Fräulein might catch you,' he warned.

'That's very good of you, Dave, but what about when you come off watch at four a.m.?' I queried.

'Don't be a silly bugger,' said the Third. 'I'll sleep on the settee in your cabin. Now off you go, otherwise you'll keep her waiting.'

I showered as quickly as possible and returned to my cabin, praying and hoping that she would accomplish a safe undetected arrival.

She apparently had. 'My poor love,' she said. 'You look absolutely shattered.'

We had a quick drink in my cabin then, after I'd checked the lie of the land, we moved into the Third Engineer's cabin.

'Golly,' she exclaimed, 'looks as if the Third Engineer has raided the galley and the bar.'

'Hell, I'm a lucky man to have a shipmate like the Third and a lovely lass like you,' I said.

'That's quite right,' she said, 'but all talk and no action is not what we want, is it, Paul?'

142

The footsteps were unmistakable. We'd both awakened almost simultaneously.

'Quiet, quiet,' I whispered, glancing at the cabin door to check that it was securely locked. Then the familiar knocks, but on my own cabin door.

'Are you there, Fourth?'

It was undoubtedly the Stewardess.

'Have you got Elaine in there with you?' she demanded.

No reply, I looked at my watch: 3.20 a.m. I couldn't believe it. We held each other tight, shaking with a mixture of fear and foreboding. It was too ludicrous to be true. The knocking stopped then the Stewardess was on her way, her footsteps gradually fading away.

'What now?' said Elaine.

'God knows, but no doubt we shall find out in the morning. Until then all I can suggest is that we assume that it's our last night together,' I proposed.

'That's not a very nice thing to say, Paul,' she said.

'Sorry, my love. I didn't mean that. You know, you've made me feel very much wanted, unlike others we know,' I added.

'Touché,' she replied, smiling in her own special way.

We again awoke together, this time to knocking on the Third Engineer's cabin door. It was the Cabin Steward with tea for two.

'Been promoted then, Fourth,' he winked.

'Er, oh no, I guess not, but thanks for the tea,' I stumbled out.

My mind was now racing. What to do for the best? Elaine dressed as quickly as she could and departed on a pre-planned route to try and get back to her cabin undetected. I entered my own cabin as quietly as possible to avoid disturbing the Third Engineer and quickly changed into my working gear ready to go on watch.

I started to walk down the alleyway towards the messroom. Then I heard, once again, that familiar booming voice at the end of our alleyway. My heart missed more than one beat.

'Look, Chief,' he thundered. 'He wasn't in his cabin at three twenty this morning.'

'I see,' answered the Chief. 'And you checked that for yourself, then?'

'No, of course I didn't, Chief, but that doesn't alter the situation one iota.'

'Well,' said the Chief, 'before you come sounding off down here about the whereabouts of the Fourth Engineer at three twenty in the morning, I would suggest that you speak to him personally and no doubt he will explain what he was doing.'

By now the Chief had raised his voice to a level that could be heard right down the alleyway, presumably in the knowledge that I would be bound to hear him.

He continued. 'I turned him out personally to deal with problems we were having with the sewage disposal plant and he has spent half the night up to his eyes in it.'

Yes, Chief, I chuckled to myself, that's quite true, except my eyes were not quite where you are suggesting. He still hadn't finished.

'Does that explain his whereabouts or do I have to order him here to tell you personally?' he finally added.

I didn't wait to hear the Old Man's reply but dashed down the alleyway back to my cabin and jumped onto my settee, completely forgetting the poor Third Engineer.

'Bloody hell,' groaned the Third Engineer. 'Haven't you had enough, Paul?'

'Sorry, Dave, it's a bloody emergency. If the Old Man asks you where I've been, I've spent half the night in the engine room fixing the sewage plant, according to the Chief. Don't forget, will you?'

He started to laugh then rolled off my settee and collapsed on the floor, convulsed.

'Ye gods,' he stammered out, 'I've heard it called all kinds of things but now I've heard it all.'

By good luck or good fortune, it turned out that the Chief's explanation was accepted by the Old Man and Elaine and I lived to see another day.

17

I couldn't help but reflect on the irony that now I was sailing on a vessel which frequently returned to its home port, I was carless, although my motorbike at least enabled me to get around town with a fair degree of ease. As the colder weather started to make its presence uncomfortably felt, I decided the time had come for me to tackle my car engine. There was no doubt at all that the engine required to be completely dismantled and it seemed to make good sense to remove the complete transmission unit, including the clutch, gearbox and overdrive, at the same time and deal with the lot at one go. After an almighty struggle and the use of every imaginable piece of gear I could lay my hands on, I managed to extract the various units, mainly from beneath the car after raising the front to a height where the rear bumper was touching the garage floor. What then followed was a continual import and export of mainly used but occasionally new engine parts as I took them with me to carry out the repairs in my off-watch periods while at sea.

HM Customs and Excise were frequently mystified by my disclosures at the start but, as time wore on, they even became interested enough to enquire as to the progress with the repairs. They, like others that were intrigued with my venture, were possibly convinced that the whole lot would never come together again and couldn't resist gloating over the impending doom. I hadn't intended, originally, to carry out all of the repairs myself and, in any event, was faced with having the engine reboring work carried out by specialists who mischievously convinced me that a slight increase in the compression ratio of the engine would help to increase the performance. Of course that suggestion necessitated even more machining operations but, as they were also extremely enthusiastic or at least curious about the outcome, I agreed to let them perform in the manner they wished.

I had fortunately acquired a number of manufacturers' service manuals which helped me to set up the various assemblies in the required manner and, in order to make the reassembly more straightforward, I built up the whole transmission system on the garage floor before trying to relocate the lot in the car. No doubt any self-respecting garage mechanic would have had kittens if he had witnessed what followed. Sufficient to say that untangling a few balls of tangled-up knitting wool would have been easier by far, but after a few well-chosen words and blasphemies and not an unreasonable amount of good fortune, I had the lot in place and finally lined up and secured. Certain important settings and adjustments had been rammed down my throat by not just one or two 'experts' and I tried my best to fulfil all of these requirements to the letter of the law, so to speak.

Then came the big day when the proof of the pudding was about to be exposed, for better or worse. I'd decided not to replace the bonnet until I'd convinced myself that all was running satisfactorily, so when I turned the ignition key for the first time, I had a panoramic view of chariots of fire as the engine tried to fire and ignite the carburettor, the timing somehow or other being hopelessly adrift. It was also obvious that the engine was barely turning over despite the battery being fully charged.

Then the penny dropped. Whilst I could adjust the timing, there was little I could do to relieve the problem with the engine turning over too slowly. Thanks to the specialist's handiwork, the starter motor could not cope with the increased compression ratio of the engine. By very good fortune, one of my brothers-in-law was in a position to get my starter motor specially rewound with heavy-duty windings but, even after that, the engine did not turn over at any great speed.

To say I was delighted with the outcome of the repairs would have been the understatement of the year. Not only had I learnt a lot, even despite a few hiccups, I had avoided any major pitfalls and, even more importantly, restored my car to a roadworthy condition. The increased performance was something that I was look-

146

ing forward to although I wasn't entirely convinced that the transmission system would be able to withstand the extra stress and strain. Time would tell but at least I would have an enjoyable time, hopefully, finding out.

The question then arose as to whether or not I should keep my newly refurbished car or trade it in, while the going was good, for a newer and less used model. Just about that time, the Rootes Group were announcing plans to replace the current Sunbeam Alpine with a restyled version, the new models losing the distinctly different rising rear wings which gave the car a heads-down appearance. The new model, however, had an equally impressive appearance and was certainly very sleek, incorporating a detachable hardtop and improved performance, with an increased size of engine. To help me make up my mind, I made an appearance in the local dealer's showrooms. I was extremely impressed with the new model but far from happy about the salesman's reaction when I advised him that I had a much earlier version to trade in which performed very well after its overhaul. The best advice he could give me was to consider taking it to a specialist sports car dealer and offering it for a cash settlement. It turned out that the dealer most likely to be really interested in the car was based in the south of England and I had no immediate plans to return to those parts at that time. I just prayed and hoped that I could maintain the car at its peak performance until I had the opportunity to change it. In any event, time was marching on, Christmas was looming and more urgent matters were demanding attention.

One of the disadvantages of being a seafarer is that quite often you are in the wrong place at the wrong time and probably more so at Christmas than at any other time. Therefore, it was with mixed feelings that I learned our Christmas this year would be spent in Gothenburg but, as the saying goes, every cloud has its silver lining, and that happened to be the good news about the Captain being relieved for the Christmas period, together with the Chief Engineer. At least for one voyage, a less severe and daunting atmosphere would exist, with life hopefully conducted in a much lighter vein.

As usual, even over Christmas, there was a full complement of passengers, many who repeated the same routine year after year, obviously convinced they were getting very good value for their money.

Whilst I had no plans to risk my arm or whatever once again with the opposite sex on board the vessel, even with the Old Man at a safe distance, I was looking forward to a less pressureful existence.

Probably it was that new-found freedom that tempted me to be a bit too resourceful when ordered by the relief Chief Engineer to calm things down at the Third Engineer's Christmas Eve party. Everything had been going with a swing until the Second Mate decided it was time for him to impersonate a female stripper.

For my part, I wasn't overimpressed with the Second Mate's attitude to life; my feelings were heightened that evening by the choice mix of drinks I'd been liberally partaking of, so when activated by the Chief's personal orders, I unfortunately made a somewhat bad choice of implements to dampen the Second Mate's ardour. On reflection, the Chief had more than likely intended that I simply aim and deposit the remaining contents of my glass in the direction of his posterior, but I had a flash of inspiration. I slipped out of the cabin, unhooked the nearest fire extinguisher and sneaked back in, taking careful aim and considering the rapidly moving target, scored more or less a direct hit, to the cheers of one and all – minus one, of course. In my haste to arm myself, I inadvertently had chosen a foam extinguisher which, quite properly, did not respond to my attempts to stop it performing with great abandon. The Third Engineer's cabin and all present were being rapidly decorated in an ever-enlarging foam coating. I dashed, panic-stricken, with the extinguisher still pouring out its contents, to the engineers' bathroom and poked the live end out of an open porthole, to the amazement of a young couple strolling along the quay. I hauled it back in then pointed it down the loo as, at last, it ran out of chemicals.

'You silly sod,' bawled the Second Engineer. 'You better get cleaning up this mess before you-know-who finds out and reports you to the Old Man when he returns.'

It's quite amazing what a guilty conscience and a threat to one's livelihood can do to motivate an active clean-up operation, which

I tackled with unbelievable gusto, convinced that if I failed, my seagoing career would be over, once and for all.

Needless to say, the Second Mate didn't have much sympathy for my plight but, strangely enough, we got on a whole lot better afterwards. Having apparently survived this escapade unscathed, I decided that discretion in future would be better than valour. Then the Chief Engineer suddenly decided he had a good-Samaritan role to fulfil. Our young Irish Radio Officer had apparently decided that life was no longer worth living and climbed to the top of the shore crane next to the vessel. The Chief followed him but dressed only in his underpants.

'I don't believe it,' moaned the Second Engineer. 'You nearly suffocating us with the contents of that bloody fire extinguisher and now the Chief trying to kill himself up a ruddy crane. Don't you dare go climbing up there, understood?' he added forcibly.

'No, way, Sec,' I replied. 'I've learnt my lesson the hard way, I can assure you. But what about the Chief?'

'I haven't a clue but we'd better go and have a look and see how he's getting on.'

The biting-cold air hit us as we ventured on deck. A crowd had gathered on the quay, their upturned faces staring in bewilderment, anxiety and amazement. Only the younger faces were captivated in sheer admiration at his audacity. The Chief had made it successfully to the top and was talking to the Radio Officer.

Then one of the elderly female passengers added her contribution. 'What else will they require the Chief Engineer to put right? The poor man, he'll get his death of cold in this weather dressed like that.'

Then bells started ringing but, despite it being Christmas Eve, the bells didn't emanate from the nearby church but the Gothenburg Fire Brigade obviously responding to a call from a well-meaning bystander.

The two daredevils descended with a rapidity that must have even surprised them. Only the fact that they were both nearly frozen stiff saved them from recriminations from the fire officers but at least the Chief got a resounding cheer from the spectators, who obviously decided they'd witnessed a truly heroic mission.

But the Chief was far from finished. If he was having to spend

149

Christmas away from his home and family, he wasn't going to sit around moaning and complaining. No, sir. Christmas night was to be a party night with a difference. His cabin was the venue and his guests included what appeared to be about half the female nursing staff of the local hospital.

It looked as if the Chief had made a wise choice with his guests, with their professional services being more than likely required before the evening was over. He had decided that there was only one game to be played, in heats with both single sex and mixed teams taking part in turn. The objective of the game was simplistic in the extreme. How many persons could be accommodated in his double bunk, with time playing no insignificant part in deciding the winners.

Whilst the all-female team were the outright winners overall, the heat generated in the mixed team competition tended to suggest that delaying tactics were being employed by those in the deepest entanglement of arms, legs and any other parts that came into unavoidable contact with one another. In the end, it only seemed fair that the Chief's chosen team should win the mixed team competition. He wasn't complaining about being squashed alive by a wholesome bevy of gorgeous Swedish females. They decided that he should have a unique epitaph. Possibly the only dead gent to have his life terminated simultaneously by 11 girls in bed with him at the same time. If he had been freezing to death the previous evening, his temperature tonight was likely to hit the roof to guarantee his survival. As often is the case, he who dares, wins – and he did.

Whatever else happened over Christmas, ashore or afloat, the Chief's party would be the highlight for us all.

Probably one of the most beneficial aspects of sailing into Gothenburg was the location of the vessel's berth. This was almost in the city centre, with the main shopping and entertainment facilities just a few minutes' walking distance away. Not only did this provide a very welcome break from shipboard routine whenever the opportunity arose to get ashore, another significant advantage of the close proximity of these facilities was that in the middle of winter, when the air temperatures are well below freezing point, one could reach the warmth of the nearest store without suffering undue discomfort. Having safely reached this warm haven, there was usually a marked reluctance to venture further afield if the purchases you were after could be readily obtained, even if it meant paying a little more than elsewhere. I was frequently mystified by the apparent need of the shoppers to be almost baked to a turn in the large department stores with the heating turned up to maximum levels. Obviously the locals were determined to forget their hostile winter climate once indoors and the shop owners duly obliged their whims and fancies with what could possibly be best described as oven-hot atmospheres, which also probably accounted for their deathly pallor.

Venturing further afield during winter usually only meant finding the nearest tram stop. The fact that trams, trains, cars and lorries, also taxis and the odd bus or two, not only managed to keep running despite the cold and snowfall, but with usually little or no delay, speaks volumes for the attitude of the authorities. What was more surprising than anything else was the dexterity of the drivers in controlling their vehicles, whether on road or rail track. I would stand in amazement watching a vehicle approach a road junction at what seemed far too great a speed to be able to stop without skidding on the slippery surfaces and just when it seemed that an accident was inevitable, the front wheels of the vehicle would flick from hard left to hard right, creating a remarkable braking effect with the snow piling up rapidly in front. Even in these circumstances, with the front wheels not contributing anything to steering, the vehicle would remain travelling in a straight line and never once did I witness a collision or accident in these difficult and testing conditions.

Having said that, I very nearly contributed to the Swedish road accident statistics in similar circumstances to those drivers whose attention was distracted in the UK by the miniskirted girl brigade. These girls left nothing to the imagination in the nether regions. In my case, the lady in question appeared, at first glance, to be naked from her blouse downwards. As my head swivelled involuntarily in her direction and my eyes struggled to focus on her erogenous zone, my legs lost their sense of direction and I will forever remain indebted to a Swedish gentleman who hoisted me, literally by my coat-tails, out of the path of a tram. Her only crime had been to wear the tightest pair of flesh-coloured ski trousers I had ever seen.

We all knew that the living standards in Scandinavia were well in advance of our own, with pay and working conditions leaving us well behind. This was obvious whenever one purchased goods in the shops or sought a little light entertainment ashore in one form or another. The cost of alcohol was almost prohibitive and only the cinemas seemed prepared to offer value for money based on our standards. Despite the cost involved, the locals certainly didn't deprive themselves of entertainment, although it was fairly true to say that there were times when they couldn't help getting other unsuspecting individuals involved. It was not unusual to discover that the husbands and wives present were not maritally related, the Swedes surely being the originators of the wife-swapping scenario. Unless one was prepared to become involved in domestic warfare, any offer to join their ranks was best politely refused. Those invitations usually only surfaced as the parties were leaving the establishments, sometimes in disarray after consuming well over their alcoholic capabilities and looking for alternative partners for the evening. On occasions the lack of domestic bliss produced a hurry-up wagon, more than adequately manned by a fully armed complement of police officers, their arms consisting of extremely menacing swords, which they had been known to wield, not in vain.

But Gothenburg was not all about drunken orgies, womanising or even chief engineers climbing dock cranes. The buildings, many of very early origin, were on a scale that blended well with the surrounding environment, and the parks and open spaces helped to give the city a quite homely atmosphere, quite unique in my experience at that time. The change of seasons are not only rapid but almost indiscernible, with spring and autumn happening almost overnight. As the summer advances, one of the most popular places to visit is the Liseberg entertainment park, on a scale almost unheard of in our country in that era. Apart from the usual attractions, the Liseberg had both outdoor theatre facilities as well as indoor amenities, rivalling the best of anything else on the Continent.

152

The Third Engineer, who was a keen jazz fan and with an ear to the latest attractions visiting the park, decided to procure two tickets for him and me to see the fabulous Duke Ellington Orchestra during their forthcoming tour of Scandinavia.

'Don't you think it's a bit of a risk, Dave?' I said. 'Knowing our luck, we'll be on our way down the Mediterranean by this time next month.' I was only thinking of the outlay, which was not inconsiderable.

'Look, Paul, they probably won't get to the UK, so I reckon it's worth the risk. Anyway, if we can't go, we should be able to get the ship's agent to sell the tickets for us.'

Our luck held. There we were, just a few weeks later, sat in the third row from the front with the real, living, Duke about to make his entry to an enthralled, entranced and worshipping audience, to front the band of the decade.

The applause thundered around the auditorium as the band launched into its first number. Pure joy as the familiar sounds reverberated around us, absolute heaven, the real thing. Even the audience couldn't remain seated, those towards the back crept forwards along the aisles towards the stage.

'Never seen that before, Paul. It's strange they don't stay seated,' the Third offered as a comment on the passing scene, so to speak.

After only three numbers, with everything going apparently well and the most delightful melodic sounds filling the auditorium, the music suddenly stopped for no apparent reason, then the orchestra trooped off the stage.

'What the hell's going on, Dave?' I asked.

'Search me. Probably the police have stopped it because of the audience blocking the aisles,' Dave replied.

'No,' said the Swedish fan sat next to me. 'They have stopped playing because the microphones for the solo instruments have gone kaput. That means the people sat at the back have only been hearing the backing.'

I thanked him for explaining the situation to us.

'Now what?' I said. 'A lot of money for not a lot of music.'

But no sooner had I got the words out of my mouth than an announcement was made in Swedish to the audience. My Swedish neighbour explained that the orchestra were moving to the nearby dance hall and a limited number of the audience would be allowed in. Those who couldn't get in would be invited to attend the following night to see the orchestra in a repeat concert in the outdoor theatre, all free of charge.

'Right, come on, Paul. Let's see if we can get into the dance hall.'

We did, and enjoyed a totally different and unexpected musical feast demonstrating the undoubted capability of the instrumentalists. Then, being gluttons for more of the same music, we turned up the following evening for the free concert and were treated to another musical feast.

My everlasting memory of that concert is watching the great man himself picking his nose with one hand as he conducted his orchestra with the other. His timing was perfect ... with both hands.

18

Whilst my social life on the *Lara* was under an enforced embargo regarding any fun and games with the opposite sex, the same could not be said to apply during my regular trips home between voyages. Despite my previous misadventures with his girlfriend, my pal Geoff and I grasped just about every available opportunity we could to enjoy the company of the girls he seemed able to produce from nowhere, not unlike the proverbial conjuror with rabbits out of his hat. Neither of us was foolish enough to drink excessively when driving but when I look back at those times, I shudder at the risks that many drivers took. The rule that applied if stopped by a police officer when suspected of being over a reasonable limit was to be able to walk along a narrow chalk line without wavering or going off course. Provided one could overcome that obstacle and no traffic offence had been committed, a good ticking-off and warnings about no further repetition of the transgressing behaviour would end the matter. On one occasion, after leaving a city centre pub with our respective girlfriends and jumping in our cars with the intention of following one another, we set off unbelievably in opposite directions, then the penny dropped and almost simultaneously we each stopped our cars and executed rapid three-point turns, only to find ourselves passing each other going in opposite directions. Unfortunately for us, the long arm of the law had witnessed the spectacle from his push-bike and took an awful lot of convincing that we were neither drunk and incapable nor slightly off our rockers. I recall little of the ensuing evening's frolics and was somewhat taken by surprise by my father's questioning the following day after I had arisen with a heavy head and a sickly stomach.

155

'Paul, how come you parked your car last night in the garage the opposite way round to usual?' he asked.

I couldn't even remember the drive home, let alone parking the car in the garage. At first I thought he was joking but then realised that it must have seemed to him an extremely tricky manoeuvre to accomplish in the darkness, taking into consideration the somewhat torturous approach even when driving straight in as usual.

'Well, dad, if you never try these manoeuvres, you don't find out if they're possible,' I lied.

He was far from convinced by my explanation but did not pursue the matter any further, thankfully.

I'd had a long-standing invitation from my previous colleague, the Third Engineer on the *Leo*, who had abandoned his seagoing career after leaving that vessel, to marry his fiancée. Ted and his new wife lived just up the coast in his former home town. He'd been absent for a number of years following a national newspaper exposure of his somewhat staggeringly frank outburst in front of one of the country's leading judges in the High Court in London when a typically vindictive barrister attempted to accuse him of wrongdoing. Ted was an honest-as-the-day-is-long individual and had no intention of putting up with any nonsense from the opposition, no matter how learned they were.

The problem for him was that he was on a hiding to nothing, regardless of his own frankness and truth about the matter in hand. After all, he was not going to be in a position to prove, one way or another, whether he knew the Lord Mayor's boat had such a rotten bottom that the engine would fall through it when Ted was lifting the boat out of the harbour for its winter lay-up. What got Ted's dander up was the suggestion that he'd not taken sufficient precautions prior to lifting the boat.

It was when Ted tried to cross-examine the plaintiff's barrister that the roof fell in on him, so to speak, with the judge warning him in no uncertain terms about contempt of court. Ted's contempt for the court should have been unprintable but the national press deemed otherwise.

All of that was then deep in the recesses of my mind when I next spoke to him and got the all-clear for a visit, which I had naturally thought would include his new wife in so far as entertainment was concerned. Not wishing to be a lone ranger in their company, I suggested to Ted that I bring one of my female friends with me.

'Paul, what a daft suggestion, if you don't mind me saying. How the hell are we supposed to enjoy ourselves if we've got to be on our best behaviour all the time?'

I'd learnt, from previous experience, not to challenge the great man's edicts, so I sped over to his home town to be greeted like a long lost comrade in arms.

His wife seemed even more stunningly attractive than when I last saw her over a year previously. But any thoughts that she was going to join us on our spree were soon dispelled when she excused herself to leave to join her own group of friends for their own night out.

'Come on, Paul, there isn't time to sit around here losing good drinking time.'

As his wife had taken their car, I was delegated as chauffeur and therefore had the daunting task of trying to measure my liquid intake in relation to the drinking time left before the pubs closed.

Ted's idea was to travel first to the farthest-flung pub he knew in the area then work our way back homeward-bound so he could collapse on his doormat with relative ease. What staggered me most about the evening was the vast number of people he was acquainted with. There was not a single pub out of the seven or so we visited that didn't have patrons present who knew Ted as a bosom friend. As the evening wore on, my sides ached from laughing at the non-stop jokes that escaped from Ted's jolly friends, and it was only when the words 'Time, ladies and gentlemen, please', resounded around the walls of the pub just round the corner from his home that Ted suggested the night was still young yet and he knew yet another establishment that didn't quite adhere to the licensing laws, time-wise.

By that time I decided that no way was I chancing my arm at any more driving and if we were to venture forth yet again, it would have to be either on shank's pony or by taxi. Ted was not at all happy about spending money on road transport but as he had no intention of walking to our next venue, suggested that we go to his home to telephone for transport.

As we entered his house, the most delightful aromas wafted in

157

our direction. In the kitchen, his dear wife was busily concocting a feast of a supper which she knew darn well was sufficient of a magnet to keep her husband at home. It was suggested that I should probably stay the night rather than risk driving home, but as I had a pressing meeting to attend the following day and as the supper helped sober me up, and with a strict promise that I would not exceed 30 miles an hour on the homeward trip, I bade them farewell. It was around 3.00 a.m. and I didn't see a single vehicle on the roads in the 40-mile journey home. Whenever the temptation to go a little faster reared its head, I eased my foot off the accelerator, remembering my promise to my friends, and, sure enough, reached home without a single drama.

As I was one of a few of the officers on the vessel to own a car, I offered lifts into the city from the vessel's home port berth, to save taxi fares. It didn't take long and it was an excuse to get a break from the relatively boring routine on board in port. My passengers included the Chief Engineer, whose home was on the opposite side of the city in the leafy suburbs – and he expected to be taken all the way home. That was a much longer journey time and left me feeling somewhat guilty about abandoning my post for that length of time. Whenever the situation was likely to happen, I made sure that my duties were being fully covered by one of the other engineers on board.

Therefore all should have been well but, like everything else in this world, Sod's Law can and does frequently prevail, no matter what. We were due to take fuel bunkers on board the following day, so in order to make this operation more straightforward and with the blessing of the Chief, I had started transferring fuel between tanks. Then the Chief decided he would like to be transported home a little earlier than usual so I instructed a relief engineer to continue with the fuel-transferring in my absence.

On returning to the vessel, I was greeted with a scene more reminiscent of an erupting oilfield, with bodies flying in all directions trying to stem the flow of the black treacly substance escaping from the deck scuppers into the dock and covering the water surface with a thick black film.

I stared in total disbelief at the scene before me then shot down below to find that the relief engineer had completely forgotten the transfer was taking place. I stopped the transfer pump and then literally exploded on the spot, telling him to pack his bags, report straight to the company's superintendent and explain to him what had happened. Even in those days, fouling of dock waters usually resulted in a heavy fine for the guilty parties and I was determined not to be blamed for this disaster.

The Chief was obviously extremely upset when he found out the following day what had happened and decided that, in future, only ship's engineers would carry out fuel transfers, even if it meant him having to go without his lift.

By the time we were due to depart for our next voyage, all traces of the oil spill had been completely removed but the repercussions were still making themselves felt, with strict orders from the company to adhere to port regulations at all times when dealing with fuel operations.

Just before we sailed, I unexpectedly received a letter from Elaine, my schoolteacher acquaintance from an earlier voyage, who told me that she was due to take part in a teaching course at Leeds University and wondered if I would like to join her in Leeds if I could get some leave. According to our sailing schedule, we were due to be in our home port while she was in Leeds, but whether I could get a few days off, I just didn't know. The thought of a few days in her company once again without the Fräulein breathing down one's neck was enough to encourage me to ask the Chief if he had any objection to me being excused duties for three days. On revealing the reasons for my request, the Chief agreed, subject to me being formally relieved by the company.

One thing for certain, the winter had once again returned with a vengeance. Ice conditions in the Skagerrak and Kattegat were as severe as any within living memory. The Baltic Sea froze over and in order to enable trade to continue between Finland and Sweden, convoys of lorries amazingly drove over the ice fields, guided by pilots and lighted beacons, with refuelling points at intervals during the crossings.

Our only hope of making progress in these conditions was to proceed in a convoy with an ice-breaking vessel leading the way. We were due to sail from Gothenburg but were delayed because of loading some last-minute cargo.

The Chief looked quite concerned. 'We've missed the convoy, Fourth, but the Old Man is still determined to sail as scheduled. If the ice is as bad as the coastal station is broadcasting, then we could be in for a difficult passage out of the Kattegat. If you have any difficulty, like losing the sea cooling effect if the sea injection de-icing fails, then let me know immediately.'

'I certainly will, Chief. I've never experienced steaming in bad ice before.'

I had no idea what to expect but I had also heard the reports of the worsening ice conditions, and as we manoeuvred away from the berth, feelings of apprehension began making themselves evident.

I didn't have long to wait. Already the bridge had ordered full ahead on the main engines when normally we would just be gradually gathering forward momentum. The noise was deafening in the engine room as the hull hammered into the ice. The shell plating on both sides of the vessel deflected inward to alarming extents.

'Hells bells, Donks, much more of this and we'll be out of action. Just look how close the main switchboard is now to the ship's side. Go and get the Chief down below as quick as you can.'

Before I could say any more, the engine room started to fill with steam. The sea cooling water had obviously stopped circulating through the main condenser, the vacuum was dropping rapidly and I was forced to disengage the turbine machinery to avoid serious damage occurring. I then eased the speed control valve in for the reciprocating machinery and rang the engine room telegraph to half ahead.

The response from the bridge was immediate. The telephone rang out.

'What the hell do you think you are doing, Fourth?' The Captain's unmistakable growls rang in my ears.

'We've got problems, sir, we can't maintain the main engine speed. In fact, I soon shan't be able to see down here. The exhaust

160

steam from the engine plant is not being condensed because we've no cooling water.'

'I'm not concerned with your problems, Fourth. Just put those engines back to full ahead immediately, otherwise we are not going to get through this ice. That's an order. Do you understand?'

'If you say so, Captain.' I swung the telegraph back to full ahead and opened up the control valve to the maximum position just as the Chief Engineer hit the plate level alongside me. Without saying a word, he swung the telegraph to slow ahead and eased in the control valve once again then telephoned the bridge.

Before he could open his mouth, the familiar growl made its presence felt yet again.

'Fourth, I'll wring your bloody neck if you don't stop reducing the engine speed. Do I make myself clear?'

'Chief here. Get yourself down here right away, Captain. Immediately, that is. The pilot and the Third Mate can manage for a few minutes without you.'

There was no reply. Whether it was surprise or shock at the Chief's response, I couldn't determine but shortly afterwards the familiar voice boomed down from above.

'Where are you, Chief? I can't see you or the Fourth,' he complained.

'Exactly, Captain,' answered the Chief. 'I'll come up and meet you. Stay where you are.'

What was said, I couldn't hear, but the conversation was not as heated as I'd expected.

'How did it go then, Chief?' I asked, as the Chief returned to the lower plate level.

'Well, it's now dawned on him that he's just put his vessel, and all on board, in considerable jeopardy by his stubborn actions.'

Glancing around the engine room, it was obvious that thousands of pounds of damage had been caused to the shell plating and structure. Goodness knows how much damage had been caused elsewhere.

'The Captain is not going to be very popular with his superintendents when they realise what needs to be done to put this lot back in order,' added the Chief.

By now, we'd ground to a halt but the de-icing steam was beginning to do its job. Sea water circulation was returning and the visibility in the engine room was improving.

'I'm going up to the bridge,' said the Chief. 'I'll suggest us backing and filling with the engines ahead then astern to see if we can get free, otherwise we could get badly nipped.'

As good as his word, the Chief departed. Shortly afterwards, the Chief rang down from the bridge.

'OK Fourth, listen to me carefully. Put the telegraph to standby and when the bridge respond, put the engines ahead for about half a minute then stop and go astern for the same time. Keep repeating that but there's no need to swing the telegraph each time you change engine direction. If the bridge ring "Stop" then you stop the engines and wait for further orders. Have you got that? Tell the fireman and donkeyman what's going on. Now get to it sharpish before the ship's jammed fast. I'm going down to main deck level to see if we're winning but I'll be back down below shortly.'

'How long are we supposed to keep this up?' asked the donkeyman. He was pouring copious quantities of lubricating oil on the engine bearings whenever he could get the opportunity. 'Probably would be better if we tried to get back to the berth,' he added.

'That's the problem, Donks, we can't. We've got to try and keep moving, otherwise, according to the Chief, we're in real trouble.'

'You know, Fourth, I'll bet you there's a Russian nuclear ice-breaker out there in the Kattegat but this Old Man is too bloody proud to ask for help.'

'I wouldn't argue about that. He'd sooner put us all through this misery than admit defeat.'

And he did. Our efforts continued unabated, watch after watch, for around 12 hours until there was no way ahead and we finally stopped. There we were, stuck in the middle of the Kattegat, marooned in a massive ice floe which even the ice-breakers weren't having any success with.

There was no real danger to the vessel but the sheer frustration of not being able to make progress even affected the passengers, with uncustomary criticisms of the Deck Department for landing us in the mess we were in.

When we were finally clear of the ice field, it transpired that a Russian ice-breaker had stayed clear of us. They had probably overheard some of our radio transmissions.

19

I suppose it was not too surprising that we saw little of the Captain during our voyage home. According to the Third Mate, he was constantly referring to the poor performance of the Engineering Department and blaming one and all for the delays we had encountered, regardless of the true facts of the matter. None of us were sorry that the voyage was nearing its end but, surprisingly enough, the passengers had no complaints, presumably because they had an extra day's holiday at no extra expense.

On reaching home, there was another letter for me from Elaine, reminding me of her impending trip to Leeds. As the saying goes, every cloud has a silver lining and, ironically enough because of the damage to the vessel and the need for dry-docking and repairs, I managed to escape to Leeds. I had arranged to meet her off the train at the central station and my pulse was racing as the train drew to a halt and I desperately tried to spot her amongst a sea of faces moving rapidly towards the barriers.

The relief of recognising her was like a ton weight being lifted off my shoulders. Then she noticed me and waved excitedly, we met at the barrier and I grasped both of her hands and took her suitcases off her.

'Right on time,' I exclaimed. 'It's great to see you again, Elaine. Have a good trip?'

'I wondered if you would bother to turn up. It's lovely to see you and, yes, the trip was OK.'

We walked to my car parked round the back of the station and chattered non-stop about everything under the sun. Once sat in the car, I had to admit that I hadn't had time to reserve any accommodation for us but Elaine told me that, if necessary, she could stay in college lodgings but that wouldn't include me, of course. Working on the basis that it would be easier to get a room on the outskirts of the city and after buying a hotel and accommodation guide, we commenced what I had expected would be a relatively simple and pleasant task. My main concern was not stumbling as I introduced myself and my newly acquired 'wife' to the receptionist, requesting a double-bedded room with a view if at all possible.

The smile was pleasant enough but there was a distinct doubt in her voice as she profusely expressed her regret about no room being available, at least with a double bed. I experienced considerable embarrassment when I realised that I had not covered myself with glory and we left feeling somewhat disillusioned.

'What now?' Elaine enquired. 'You must try and relax when asking for a room. That woman must have made up her mind about us as we walked up to the reception desk.'

'Guess so, Elaine. I'll get better as I keep trying.' I couldn't have known how prophetic those words were to become as we drove off to our next attempt.

'This looks more like it,' I said, as I swept confidently into the drive of a splendid-looking hostelry on the northern outer ring road.

We were met by a doorman who carried our bags to the reception desk, presumably assuming that we had already reserved our accommodation in advance. This time I didn't mess around and managed, quite confidently, to establish a quite reasonable excuse for my 'wife" and me not only being in Leeds but being left stranded by a hotel which had double-booked our reserved room.

'That is absolutely dreadful, sir. We would be delighted to offer you a room if we had one available but we really are completely full, I'm afraid. You are aware, I take it, that almost every hotel room will be booked this week in the Leeds area with the Ideal Home Exhibition running, also at least three symposiums of international importance.'

I tried not to look aghast at this news. 'Yes, my wife and I were aware of that. That's why we booked in advance. Have you any idea where we may find a room for the night until we can sort out alternative accommodation?'

'I can only suggest a city centre area hotel as they do frequently get cancellations from businessmen, but they will probably only be able to offer you single-bedded rooms,' she replied.

I thanked the receptionist for her genuine concern and help and we departed, once again feeling not only frustrated but very much defeated.

'I'm not going to be beaten. We can only try what that receptionist suggests. What a week you chose to do your ruddy course,' I added.

'Thanks, Paul, just like a man to say that. I'll have you know I hadn't a clue about what was happening in this area and the university didn't mention it either. I suppose they weren't planning on their students having a jolly whilst on the course,' she replied.

'No, I guess you're right. We'll head for the centre and see what comes up,' I said, not at all convincingly.

After trying three more establishments which claimed they were also fully booked, I was almost on the point of taking her to the university and abandoning ship. We were parked outside the central law courts looking across the road at what can only be described as a somewhat seedy establishment, badly in need of a coat of paint and a good scrub-up of its stonework. About the only thing that appeared inviting about the place was the mellow glow of the lights within.

'What do you reckon then, Elaine? Hardly the Ritz or the Waldorf Astoria but I suppose beggars can't be choosers.'

She agreed and we made our way over with our bags and entered. I felt as if I'd been married for a lifetime and had no difficulty in explaining our predicament to the lady proprietor, who could well have just stepped off stage after acting in a Victorian melodrama. Even her stern approach didn't throw me. I'm no actor but she totally misinterpreted my state of anxiety.

'You know, my dears, nobody should have to put up with what you've just been through. I can't offer you a double-bedded room tonight or even for the rest of the week, and you obviously know why. However, for tonight, I have two single rooms then from tomorrow night I can offer you a twin-bedded room. Will that be acceptable?'

By now, we'd have both accepted a stable without a manger.

'You are very kind indeed. My wife and I will be delighted to

166

accept those arrangements. What about parking my car overnight? Have you any parking space, please?'

It turned out that only on-street parking was available, which didn't fill me with confidence about my prospects of retaining my car into the foreseeable future.

'It's surprising what a bit of tasty food and a few drinks in one's belly can do for making the world seem a much more inviting place. We were both extremely tired from our exertions and bid our fellow guests goodnight, sneaking out of the bar, with a generous nightcap, to our respective rooms which, whilst on the same floor, seemed a mile apart.

'Look, Elaine, we'll make up for it tomorrow night. Anyway, you're supposed to be ready to streak off the starting blocks on your course in the morning, aren't you,' I added consolingly.

'I don't know what you had in mind for tonight, but all I want to do is to climb into a bed, single that is, in the next half-hour or so, otherwise I shall fall asleep on my feet.'

I was just about to fall off to sleep when I jerked back to consciousness, remembering that we hadn't asked for calls in the morning. I just imagined us arriving about two hours late for the start of Elaine's course with likely dire consequences for her. But what to do? Then I had a brainwave. I fumbled for some paper and a pen and wrote PLEASE CALL AT 7.00 A.M. on two pieces of paper, one for my door and one for Elaine's. I removed a drawing pin from a notice on the wall and then set off in my pyjamas, dressing gown and slippers to try and find her room. I had completely forgotten her room number, then discovered to my horror, as I traipsed round the floor, that I just couldn't recognise her room. I was on the point of giving up when the proprietor appeared, in her dressing gown, at the top of the stairs, with a very knowing look on her face.

'Naughty, naughty, young man. May I ask where you are going, because your footsteps are disturbing the guests on the floor below.'

'Oh I'm terribly sorry, I can't find my wife's bedroom. Look, I was just going to pin this notice to her door so she will get an early call,' I muttered.

I was forgiven and was assured the notice wouldn't be required,

167

so I did a quick exit off the scene and retired, once again, to my bed. By now, tiredness had overtaken me and I completely forgot my own door notice.

I awoke to a warm kiss on my cheek, a cup of tea and an urgent request to get dressed otherwise she'd be late for her course. Elaine had already partaken of breakfast, not wishing to disturb me that early. It looked as if I was going to have to sacrifice my own breakfast to get her to her course on time.

We walked slowly to the car in the bright morning sun, hand in hand, Elaine looking very businesslike in an extremely attractive suit with almost a hint of masculinity incorporated into the style.

'I don't feel all that keen about being bottled up all day in the college,' Elaine said. 'What are you going to do with yourself all day?'

'I think I will venture as far as the Ideal Home Exhibition and see what's on offer. Then you can decide if you want to go.'

After dropping her off at the university, it occurred to me that I would probably be better off without my car and returned it to its original parking place.

The scale of the exhibition surprised me but not half as much as seeing a Formula 1 racing car in the middle of the floor with just a few rope barriers separating it from an enthusiastic crowd of sightseers. I made my way over to the car and, whilst, bending over to look into the cockpit, a young man asked me about the car, which I was quite familiar with, at least from a technical standpoint.

As the questioning continued and I did my best to answer in a convincing manner, the crowd increased and I realised that, once again, I was being caught in a situation not entirely of my own making. So before my cover was blown, probably in an extremely embarrassing manner, I escaped to the toilet and out of harm's way.

After a speedy look round the exhibition, trying my best to avoid the misplaced glances of a few motor-racing pundits who must have thought I was straying off course, I departed with a handful of brochures, if only to prove my whereabouts later.

'How did it go then, Elaine?' I enquired on collecting her later at the university.

'It wasn't at all what I'd expected. Actually the lectures today were extremely interesting and were based on new teaching ideas for the future. We're supposed to be working backwards to the present time, if that makes sense,' she added.

'Not really, but then what I know about your profession doesn't amount to a great deal anyway, I'm afraid.'

The next two days were a mixture of sheer delight and extreme boredom as I tried to occupy myself whilst Elaine endured her course lectures. We even started to enjoy the hotel, particularly on the morning that Elaine had no lectures and we had a bit of a lie-in. Our bedroom window overlooked the law court entrance and we couldn't help but respond like a couple of teenagers as we spotted the red-robed judge and his entourage enter the building.

'How long do you think we would get for this close encounter?' I asked.

'At least a year; hard labour, you know,' she replied.

'You must be joking,' I responded. 'You're worth at least ten years, all of it hard.'

'You're a glutton for punishment, Paul, so I sentence you to life imprisonment.'

So that was that. But she was only joking and despite our mutual interest and concern for one another, Elaine was neither ready or prepared to sacrifice her career for me — or probably anyone else at that point in time.

It was only after I had returned home and chatted to my friend Geoff that it began to dawn on me not every girl was looking for a future partner despite their apparent keen interest in the type of encounter I'd just enjoyed.

20

My final voyage on the *Lara*, at least as Fourth Engineer, was leading up towards Christmas once again, with one big difference to the previous year. Provided we maintained our schedule, we were due to return to our home port almost on Christmas Eve, which put a considerable amount of pressure on us to perform in the best possible manner at all times to ensure this happened.

Whilst in Gothenburg, I took the opportunity to buy some of the special Nordic Christmas presents which adorned the department stores, for my family and friends. There is definitely a real sense of festivity in Scandinavia, with the family groups all striving to outdo each other, certainly enjoyment-wise, but, even as complete strangers, we did not feel out in the cold when it came down to joining in.

As we steamed away from Gothenburg for the last time, as far as I was concerned, I speculated on the possibility of me coming back at some time in the future. Unfortunately, I haven't had the good fortune to return to this fine city in the intervening years. On returning home, my friend Geoff informed me that he was emigrating to South Africa to work for the country's Milk Marketing Board. He had been persuaded that the future was full of promise in that country, despite the apartheid policy in existence, and he had the advantage of advice from an uncle who resided close to where he was heading. Naturally, I was going to miss our outings but it looked as if he was on to a winner, so I wished him the best of good fortune for the future.

Before his departure and as a belated Christmas celebration, we decided to trip the light fantastic at one of the local dance halls. Geoff, in his own inimitable way, managed to get us involved with a couple of sisters who resided in a local town. For once, Geoff hadn't chosen the most gorgeous of the two, but that wasn't bothering me at all. When it transpired that they shared a town-house and required a lift home after the dance, we almost fell over backwards to grant their wishes.

What really did surprise me was their insistence that we have a coffee with them at home before our departure. Unfortunately, I was not prepared for the ensuing events. It turned out that the sisters had been devastated by some family misfortune which had left them very much on their own. They were looking for a lot of support and love as well as happiness and must have thought that their prayers had been answered when Geoff and I appeared on the scene that night.

It was not at all easy for them to accept that fate has a funny way of not always coming up trumps and Geoff's girl was terribly upset when he told her of his impending departure abroad. As I was going to be around for a little while and as there was time for at least one more date before Geoff departed, we arranged another trip, this time out into the country.

I look back now on that day out with many happy memories but with great sadness as that was the very last time we were going to enjoy each other's company, also the company of those delightful sisters. Geoff was, tragically, the victim of a road traffic accident in South Africa when his car developed a steering fault unexpectedly and the world was robbed of a great bloke and me of a true friend.

After Geoff's departure for South Africa, I decided it was time I paid a visit again to the south, not only to see my sister and family, but also to catch up with a few of my former friends from my London sailing days.

It was during this holiday that I was to meet my first fiancée, a girl who, ironically enough, had not long returned from Africa after the tragic premature death of her father. Christine was several years younger than myself but not at all horrified by my way of life as a seafarer. We got on like a house on fire and it was extremely difficult to drag myself away and return north to work once again. Of course, I promised her that as soon as I was due more leave I would return south again, but in the meantime we would have to be satisfied with talking to each other regularly on the phone and writing to one another. There was not the slightest hint at that time that she would come to detest my seagoing career and the separations it forces on the couples and families concerned, and I couldn't wait to return to see her.

One thing was for certain; I decided that the next time I headed south by road, it would be to take my car to the specialist sports car dealer at Hendon on the outskirts of London, with the fervent hope that their offer would be sufficient to help me fund the purchase of the latest model available.

The opportunity finally came when I was ordered to London for port relief purposes on a vessel and instead of using the train, I drove there at my own expense. On the very next day, after giving it a final wash and polish and with the permission of the Chief Engineer, I drove to the dealer's taking with me all my bills for the repair work, together with the logbook and my purchase invoice. I had been warned in advance that these dealers because of their bona fide operations, would require to be completely convinced that the car was mine to sell before they would even consider making an offer.

After perusing all the paperwork, they seemed quite satisfied, then suggested that I should retire to their waiting room and help myself to a coffee whilst they took the car round the block to confirm all was in order. After a while and having drunk several coffees with no sign of them returning, I was becoming increasingly concerned. Had they been involved in an accident or blown it up? I started pacing up and down the waiting room, my anxiety increasing by the minute.

I didn't notice their return and when they entered the waiting room with beaming faces, I wondered for a minute what had happened.

'That, young man, was some test drive. We must have covered around twenty miles since we last saw you and quite frankly, its performance is quite incredible. We're able to offer you one thousand five hundred pounds which we will settle to your bank account within a week. How do you feel about that?' the salesman added.

'I thought you'd had an accident or broken down. I've been

172

fearing the worst but your offer has made up for it. Can I have something in writing that shows that you've bought the car from me for the price I've accepted?'

'No trouble at all,' was the reply, and I was even driven back to the docks, but not in my car.

When I got back on board and told my colleagues what had transpired, their response was one of scepticism and disbelief.

'You must be mad, Fourth. You won't see the colour of their money, or probably your car, again,' was the general consensus of my shipmates' opinions.

The relief duties only lasted a few days and, on returning home, there was still no evidence of my bank account having been credited with the necessary amount. My shipmates' words were beginning to sound prophetic when, out of the blue, a cheque arrived in the post for the full amount. It turned out I'd inadvertently given the car dealers incorrect bank account details, hence the payment by cheque.

I could barely wait for the cheque to clear before I presented myself, once again, to the local main Rootes Group Dealers and ordered the latest model Sunbeam Alpine, complete with a detachable hardtop. I decided to try and keep the whole thing secret from my family and friends in the south and give them, and Christine, a huge surprise on my next visit. Life was looking decidedly rosy. A new car in the offing, a new girlfriend in the south and, hopefully, promotion in the not too distant future. Time would tell whether my hopes would be fulfilled.